Hodder Gibson

Scottish Examination Mate

CW00336628

HIGHER
PHYSICS

Homework & Multiple Choice Questions for New Higher Physics

SECOND EDITION

Adrian Watt
Editor: Jim Page

Hodder Gibson

A MEMBER OF THE HODDER HEADLINE GROUP

The Publishers would like to thank the following for permission to reproduce copyright material:

Photo credits
ActionPlus (Figure 1.1, Figure 8.2, Figure 10.3); Science Photo Library (Figure 36.1, Figure 44.32–by John Durham)

Acknowledgements
Illustrations by Ian Foulis and Associates; Chartwell Illustrators; Hugh Neill and Richard Duszczak.

Every effort has been made to trace all copyright holders, but if any have been inadvertently overlooked the Publishers will be pleased to make the necessary arrangements at the first opportunity.

Although every effort has been made to ensure that website addresses are correct at time of going to press, Hodder Gibson cannot be held responsible for the content of any website mentioned in this book. It is sometimes possible to find a relocated web page by typing in the address of the home page for a website in the URL window of your browser.

Papers used in this book are natural, renewable and recyclable products. They are made from wood grown in sustainable forests. The logging and manufacturing processes conform to the environmental regulations of the country of origin.

Orders: please contact Bookpoint Ltd, 130 Milton Park, Abingdon, Oxon OX14 4SB. Telephone: (44) 01235 827720, Fax: (44) 01235 400454. Lines are open from 9.00–6.00, Monday to Saturday, with a 24-hour message answering service. Visit our website at www.hoddereducation.co.uk. Hodder Gibson can be contacted direct on: Tel: 0141 848 1609; Fax: 0141 889 6315; email: hoddergibson@hodder.co.uk

© Adrian Watt 2005
First edition published in 2000 by
Hodder Gibson, a member of the Hodder Headline Group
2a Christie Street
Paisley PA1 1NB

Impression number	10 9 8 7 6 5 4 3 2 1
Year	2010 2009 2008 2007 2006 2005

Cover photo from Science Photo Library/NASA
Typeset in 10pt Times by Fakenham Photosetting Limited, Fakenham, Norfolk.
Printed and bound in Great Britain by Arrowsmith, Bristol

A catalogue record for this title is available from the British Library

ISBN-10: 0 340-88987-X
ISBN-13: 978-0-340-88987-9

Contents

1	Distance, Displacement and Speed	1
2	Velocity and Acceleration	3
3	Motion Graphs	5
4	Equations of Motion	7
5	Projectile Motion	9
6	Scalars and Vectors	11
7	Newton's Laws	13
8	Newton 2	15
9	Impulse and Momentum	18
10	Conservation of Momentum	20
11	Energy, Work and Power	22
12	Weight and Mass	24
13	Density and Pressure	26
14	Pressure in Liquids and Gases	28
15	Flotation and Upthrust	30
16	Gas Laws	31
17	Electric Fields	33
18	Current, Voltage and Resistance	35
19	Series and Parallel Circuits	37
20	Voltage Dividers and Wheatstone Bridges	40
21	e.m.f and Internal Resistance	42
22	Electrical Energy and Power	44
23	A.C. and R.M.S. Values	46
24	Sensors, Transistors and Basic Electronics	48
25	Inverting Amplifiers – Basic Circuits	50
26	Inverting Amplifiers 2	52
27	Difference Amplifiers	55
28	Capacitance, Charge and Potential Difference	57
29	Charging Capacitors	59
30	Discharging Capacitors	61
31	Capacitors and Energy	63
32	Wave Characteristics	65
33	Snell's Law, Internal Reflection and Critical Angle	67
34	Interference	70
35	Diffraction	72
36	Irradiance and Photoelectric Effect	73
37	Emission and Absorption Spectra	75
38	Lasers and Semiconductors	77
39	p-n Junctions and Photodiodes	79
40	Nuclear Changes	82
41	Fission and Fusion	84
42	Radiation and Matter	85
43	Half-Life and Half Value Thickness	87
44	Multiple Choice and Matching Questions	89
	Formulae	129
	Answers	131

Preface

Preface

"The ants *are* a people not strong, yet they prepare their meat in the summer" Proverbs 30 v 25

The writer of this wise saying clearly believes that even the weak can benefit by timely preparation. When undertaking the Higher Physics course, practice questions are an essential part not only of the learning process but also of the preparations that must be made before taking the examination.

Homework and Multiple Choice Questions for New Higher Physics, as a companion volume for the *New Higher Physics* textbook, provides over 250 additional questions which compliment and extend the questions in the textbook. Within each of the 43 chapters the standard of the questions varies; some are designed chiefly to support learning while others will give practice of the level that will be required in the Higher Physics exam. A new chapter has been added to this second edition (44) containing multiple choice questions, numbered to correspond with the original chapters. Answers are also included. My fervent hope is that students studying Higher Physics, whether weak or strong, will find that completing the questions in this book improves their understanding of physics and improves their grade. I trust too, that teaching colleagues will find *Homework and Multiple Choice Questions for New Higher Physics* a useful addition to the available resources.

I am again indebted to Jim Page for his editorial work and for answering all of the questions. My colleague, Richard Lucas, has also helped by checking some of the numerical problems. Sandra's continuing patience and support has again been valued. While gratefully acknowledging the contribution of others, I willingly accept that the final responsibility for the content of this publication is mine.

Adrian Watt
Ratho
Edinburgh

Distance, Displacement and Speed

1 a) Write down an equation that describes how to calculate the average speed of a moving object.

b) During a 1500 m race an athlete completes the first 800 m in 2 minutes and 10 seconds.

    i) Calculate her average speed for the 800 m.

    ii) She completes the race in 4 minutes. How long does it take her to run the remainder of the race?

    iii) State whether her average speed for the final 700 m is greater or less than her average speed for the first 800 m. Justify your answer with a calculation.

c) What is her average speed for the entire race?

Figure 1.1

2 A sports scientist tries to model the motion of pitch in a game of softball. She assumes that the pitcher delivers a fast ball at a speed of $30 \, \mathrm{m \, s^{-1}}$ and that the ball travels horizontally throughout its flight. The batter stands 15 m from the pitcher.

a) How long does it take for the ball to travel from the pitcher to the batter?

b) It takes the batter 0.22 s to react to the pitcher's throw. How long does the batter have to swing the bat to hit the ball?

c) The swinging bat travels 1.4 m before hitting the ball. Calculate the speed with which the bat hits the ball.

3 A van driver makes an average of 8 deliveries per day. In a normal working week of 5 days the driver covers a total distance of 800 km.

a) Calculate the average distance travelled for each delivery.

b) The fuel consumption of the van is 7.5 km per litre. Calculate the volume of fuel used by the van in a week.

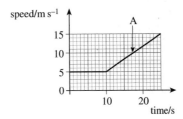

Figure 1.2

4 The graph shown in Figure 1.2 represents the motion of a train along a particular section of track.

a) What is the instantaneous speed of the train at the point marked A on the graph?

b) Calculate the distance that the train travels while moving at a constant speed.

c) Calculate the distance that the train travels while it is accelerating.

5 Which of the following has the highest average speed?

A A cyclist who completes a 15 km race in a time of 2 hours and 15 minutes.

B A runner completing an 800 m race in 1 minute and 57 seconds.

C A swimmer completing a 50 m swim in 48 s.

D A yacht sailing 7 km of a race in 1 hour 10 minutes

E A windsurfer travelling 1.2 km in 6 minutes.

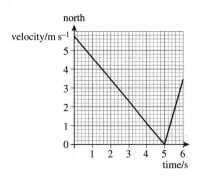

Figure 1.3

6 Figure 1.3 shows the velocity–time graph for the motion of an object initially moving due north at $5.7\,\mathrm{m\,s^{-1}}$. The speed of the object 2 s and 6 s after the start is $3.5\,\mathrm{m\,s^{-1}}$.
   a) Describe, in words, the motion of the object at time $t = 0$ seconds.
   b) Describe one difference in the motion of the object 2 s after and 6 s after the start.
   c) Calculate the distance travelled by the object during the first 2 s of the motion.
   d) Describe the displacement of the object 6 s after the start.

7 A robot in an assembly plant moves due north (a bearing of 000) for 3.4 m and then turns so as to move north east (a bearing of 045) for a further 2.6 m. The total journey takes 10 s.
   a) Calculate the total distance travelled by the robot.
   b) Calculate the resultant displacement of the robot 10 s after the start of its journey.
   c) Calculate the average speed of the robot for the total journey.
   d) Calculate the average velocity of the robot for the total journey.

8 Four pupils are trying to estimate the speed of a car along a road. The pupils position themselves on markers at intervals of 10 m along a straight section of the road. When the car reaches the first marker *all* of the pupils start their stopwatches. Each of the pupils then stops their watch as the car passes their marker.
   a) From the information given in Figure 1.4 calculate the average speed of the car.

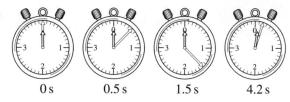

Figure 1.4

   b) Using the data given, plot a distance–time graph to show the position of the car at each of the times shown in Figure 1.4.
   c) One of the pupils looks at the graph and states that it shows that the car was slowing down towards the end of the observation. State, with reasons, whether you agree with this student.
   d) Explain why the average speed of the car over the 10 m is greater than its instantaneous speed 3 s from the start of the observation.
   e) Describe a way in which the pupils could use their stopwatches to get a more accurate measurement for the instantaneous speed of the car 3 s from the start of the observation.

9 A microlight aircraft is 50 m vertically above a marker point as it attempts to land as in Figure 1.5. The marker point is 120 m horizontally from the landing area.
   a) What is the minimum distance the microlight has to travel before reaching the landing area?
   b) At this point in the approach to landing, what is the displacement of the microlight from the start of landing area?

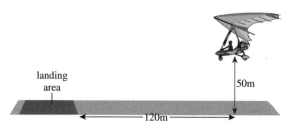

Figure 1.5

2 Velocity and Acceleration

1 a) Write a word equation defining acceleration.
  b) State a suitable unit for the acceleration of a moving object.
  c) Describe, in words, what is happening to an object moving with an acceleration of $5\,\mathrm{m\,s^{-2}}$.

The table shown in Figure 2.1 gives the speed of a car at different times as it accelerates from rest along a straight section of road.

time/s	0	1	2	3	4	5	6
speed/m s^{-1}	0	8	16	24	24	12	0

Figure 2.1

  d) Calculate the acceleration of the car during the first 2 s of the motion.
  e) Calculate the acceleration of the car during the final 2 s of the motion.

2 A cyclist travelling along a straight level road reaches a speed of $14\,\mathrm{m\,s^{-1}}$ by accelerating uniformly from rest for 3.5 s.
  a) Calculate the acceleration of the cyclist.
  b) Calculate the average speed of the cyclist during the 3.5 s he is accelerating.
  c) Calculate the distance travelled during this acceleration.

3 Describe a method, using the apparatus shown in Figure 2.2, for measuring the acceleration of a trolley down a slope. Your description should list the measurements that you will record and describe how you will calculate the acceleration from these results.

4 A cyclist, travelling north along a straight level road, reaches a speed of $10\,\mathrm{m\,s^{-1}}$ by accelerating at $2\,\mathrm{m\,s^{-2}}$ for 3 s.
  a) Calculate the velocity of the cyclist just before he starts accelerating.
  b) The cyclist continues to accelerate at the same rate for a further 2.5 s. Calculate the velocity 5.5 s after he started to accelerate.
  c) Show that the average velocity of the cyclist during the 5.5 s of this motion is $9.5\,\mathrm{m\,s^{-1}}$ due north.
  d) Draw a velocity–time graph for this motion. Mark numerical values on your graph. The time axis should extend from $t = 0$ to $t = 5.5$ s.
  e) Calculate the distance travelled by the cyclist during acceleration only.

5 Figure 2.3 shows a velocity–time graph for the motion of a trolley down an inclined runway.

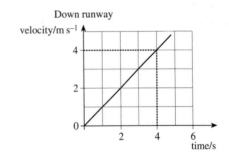

Figure 2.3

  a) What is the magnitude of the velocity 1 s after the beginning of the motion?
  b) Calculate the average velocity during the first 2 s of the motion.
  Figure 2.4 overleaf shows a velocity–time graph for a motion where after 4 s the trolley is moving away from the observation point with a speed of $4\,\mathrm{m\,s^{-1}}$.
  c) Describe, in words, how the initial motion of this trolley differs from the motion represented in the graph of Figure 2.3.

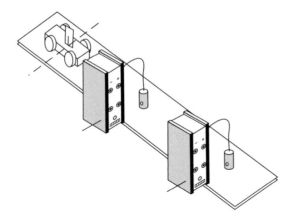

Figure 2.2

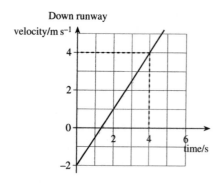

Figure 2.4

Figure 2.5 shows a situation where after 4 s the trolley is moving away from the observation point with a speed of $4\,\mathrm{m\,s^{-1}}$.

d) Describe, in words, how the initial motion of this trolley differs from the motion represented in the graphs of Figures 2.3 and 2.4.

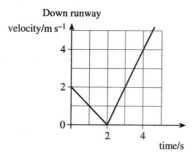

Figure 2.5

6 A light aircraft is flying with a constant velocity of $40\,\mathrm{m\,s^{-1}}$ due south (bearing 180). It is blown off course by a wind with a velocity of $10\,\mathrm{m\,s^{-1}}$ blowing *from* the north east (bearing 045).

Figure 2.6

a) Calculate the velocity of the plane as seen by an observer on the ground.

b) At one particular instant the plane is directly above a marker on the ground.
  i) How far is the plane from that marker 5 minutes later?
  ii) State the displacement of the plane relative to the marker at this time.

7 Motorcyclist A can accelerate from rest to $30\,\mathrm{m\,s^{-1}}$ in 4.4 s. Car B can accelerate from $5\,\mathrm{m\,s^{-1}}$ to $25\,\mathrm{m\,s^{-1}}$ in 4 s.

Which has the greater acceleration? Justify your answer with a calculation.

3 Motion Graphs

1 The motion of an object is represented by the velocity–time graph shown in Figure 3.1. The object is moving from left to right.

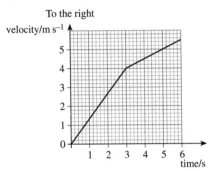

Figure 3.1

a) Copy and complete Figure 3.2 for the motion shown graphically in Figure 3.1.
b) Calculate the acceleration of the object during the first 3 s of its motion.
c) Calculate the acceleration of the object during the final 2 s of the motion shown in Figure 3.1.

time/s	0	1	2	3	4	5	6
velocity/m s^{-1}	0		2.7	4		5	

Figure 3.2

d) Calculate the distance travelled during the smaller of the two accelerations.
e) Show, by calculation, that the displacement of the object at the end of the motion shown in Figure 3.1 is 20.25 m to the right of its starting position.
f) Copy and complete Figure 3.3 to show the displacement of the object at certain times during its motion.

time/s	0	1	2	3	'4	5	6
displacement/m	0	0.65				15	20.25

Figure 3.3

2 Figure 3.4 shows the velocity–time graph for an object moving in a straight line, initially to the right and then to the left. A positive velocity means the object is moving to the right.

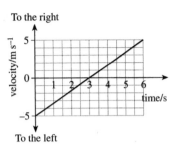

Figure 3.4

a) Show by calculation that the acceleration of the object when moving to the right is the same as the acceleration of the object as it moves to the left.
b) What feature of the graph would also lead you to the conclusion that the acceleration is the same throughout the motion?
c) The object continues to accelerate at the same rate for 2 s longer than is shown by the graph of Figure 3.4. Calculate the final velocity.

3 Figure 3.5 shows the displacement–time graph and the velocity–time graph for a certain motion.

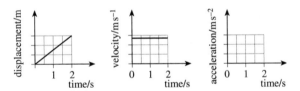

Figure 3.5

a) Copy these graphs and complete the acceleration–time graph for the same motion. Figure 3.6 again shows a pair of displacement–time and velocity–time graphs for a certain type of motion.

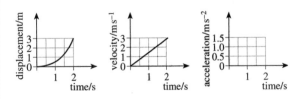

Figure 3.6

b) Copy these graphs and complete the acceleration–time graph for the same motion.

4 Figure 3.7 shows displacement–time graphs representing different types of motion.

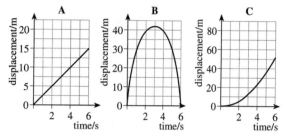

Figure 3.7

Figure 3.8 shows three tables of velocity–time data.

time/s	0	2	4	6
velocity/m s^{-1}	0	6	12	18

time/s	0	2	4	6
velocity/m s^{-1}	2.5	2.5	2.5	2.5

time/s	0	2	4	6
velocity/m s^{-1}	+30	+10	−10	−30

Figure 3.8

a) Which graph represents the motion shown by the data in the second table? Explain your answer.

b) Which graph *and* table of data represent a constant acceleration of 3 m s^{-2}? Explain your answer.

c) Which table of results shows motion in two different directions? Explain your answer.

4 Equations of Motion

1 A car moving in a straight line starts to accelerate uniformly at $4\,\mathrm{m\,s^{-2}}$. After 7 s it is travelling at a speed of $35\,\mathrm{m\,s^{-1}}$.
Which row in the following table shows the initial speed of the car and its speed 4 s after the beginning of the acceleration?

	Initial speed/$\mathrm{m\,s^{-1}}$	Speed after 4 seconds/$\mathrm{m\,s^{-1}}$
A	0	17.5
B	0	16
C	8	24
D	7	23
E	7	16

2 In Figure 4.1 an object is projected vertically upwards with an initial velocity of $44.1\,\mathrm{m\,s^{-1}}$.
a) For what time will it continue to rise? The deceleration during the upward motion is $9.8\,\mathrm{m\,s^{-2}}$.
b) What is the velocity of the object 3 s after it is projected vertically upwards?
c) How far is the object above the projection point after 3 s?
d) Calculate the maximum height reached by the object.
e) Calculate the distance travelled by the object during the first 8 s of the motion.

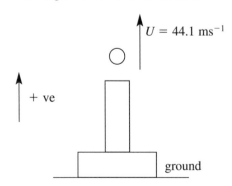

Figure 4.1

3 An object hits the ground 3.7 s after it is dropped from the top of a high building.
a) How far from the top of the building is the object 1 s after it is released?

b) What is the height of the building?
c) How far above the ground is the object 3 s after it is released?
d) What is the speed of the object just before it hits the ground?

4 A car, initially at rest, accelerates uniformly at $5\,\mathrm{m\,s^{-2}}$.
a) Calculate the speed of the car after it has travelled a distance of 40 m.
b) Calculate the speed of the car 4 s after the start of the motion.
c) When the car is 40 m away from its starting point the driver stops accelerating. The car then decelerates to rest in a further 10 s.
  i) Calculate the total time from when the car starts until it comes to rest.
  ii) Calculate how far the car is away from its starting point after 14 s.
  iii) Calculate the average speed of the car.
d) Draw a velocity–time graph for the motion of the car from the start until it comes to rest again.

5 A trolley on a slope starts from rest and reaches a speed of $0.4\,\mathrm{m\,s^{-1}}$ after it has rolled 40 cm.

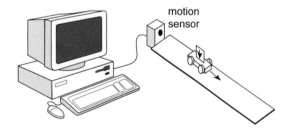

Figure 4.2

a) Calculate the acceleration of the trolley.
b) The trolley continues down the slope with the same acceleration. Calculate the speed of the trolley when it is 0.8 m from its starting point .
c) The speed of the trolley at the end of the slope is $1\,\mathrm{m\,s^{-1}}$. Calculate the length of the slope.

6 A student performing an experiment to determine the acceleration due to the force of gravity uses the apparatus shown in Figure 4.3. She records the times taken for the small steel ball to fall through certain heights.

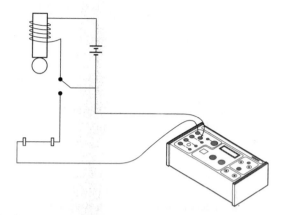

Height/m	Fall time/s				Uncertainty
	1st	2nd	3rd	mean	
0.24	0.221	0.221	0.224		
0.36	0.271	0.274	0.272		
0.44	0.301	0.299	0.302		
0.69	0.375	0.376	0.375		
0.80	0.404	0.408	0.399		
1.02	0.454	0.452	0.456		

Figure 4.3

The student repeats the measurement for each height three times.

a) Copy the table shown in Figure 4.3 and complete the table by calculating the mean time of fall for each height. Calculate the approximate random uncertainty in these mean times.

b) In her experimental report she states '*the approximate random uncertainty values confirm that the experimental method was accurate*'.

Explain, in words, what led the student to this conclusion.

c) The height fallen h and the mean fall time are connected by the equation:

$$h = \tfrac{1}{2} g t^2$$

Draw an appropriate straight line graph using the data from Figure 4.3. From the graph determine the value of g, the acceleration due to the force of gravity.

d) In her report the student states that the value for the acceleration due to the force of gravity for an object placed on the moon is ⅙ of the acceleration on the earth.

Add a line to your graph to illustrate the results that you would expect to get if this experiment were carried out on the moon.

5 Projectile Motion

1 Figure 5.1 shows a piece of apparatus used to illustrate some of the principles of projectile motion. A steel ball is held by an electromagnet 78.4 cm above a catching mechanism.

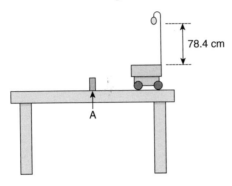

Figure 5.1

a) Show by calculation that the ball takes 0.4 s to fall from the electromagnet into the catcher.

b) In another experiment the electromagnet and catcher are mounted on top of a trolley which is placed on a horizontal frictionless track. The trolley is pushed and released so that it moves horizontally with a speed of $2\,\text{m s}^{-1}$. When the trolley passes point A the electromagnet releases the ball.

   i) How long does the ball take to fall 78.4 cm? Justify your answer.

   ii) What is the initial horizontal velocity of the ball immediately prior to its release? Explain your answer.

   iii) The ball lands in the catcher. How far is the catcher from point A when the ball first lands in it?

c) The teacher demonstrating this apparatus states that the experiment shows that *the motion of a projectile can be treated as independent horizontal and vertical motions.*

   i) Describe, in words, the *horizontal* motion of the projectile. Explain which part of the demonstration leads you to this conclusion.

   ii) Describe, in words, the *vertical* motion of the projectile. Explain which part of the demonstration leads you to this conclusion.

2 A teacher uses the apparatus shown in Figure 5.2 to demonstrate some of the principles of projectile motion. The launching mechanism, mounted on a trolley, fires a ball directly upwards with an initial vertical velocity of $3.9\,\text{m s}^{-1}$.

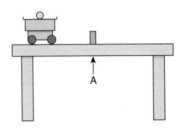

Figure 5.2

a) Show, by calculation, that the ball when fired will rise to a height of 77.6 cm above the launching mechanism.

b) Calculate the time taken for the ball to rise to its highest point above the release point.

c) The trolley is pushed so that it travels at a steady speed of $1.1\,\text{m s}^{-1}$. When the trolley passes point A the mechanism fires the ball vertically with an initial speed of $3.9\,\text{m s}^{-1}$. Calculate the distance travelled by the trolley before it catches the ball.

d) The ball is caught 2 m to the right of the launch point. Calculate the initial speed of the trolley .

3 A stunt motorcyclist jumping across a ravine, as shown in Figure 5.3, lands in the middle of the landing zone which is 23.7 m vertically below the take off point. The centre of the landing zone is 38.5 m horizontally away from the take off point.

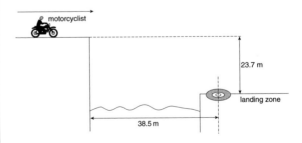

Figure 5.3

a) Calculate the time between take off and landing.

b) What is the minimum speed at take off that will ensure that the motorcyclist lands in the centre of the landing zone?

c) On one attempt, the motorcyclist has a take off speed of $30\,\mathrm{m\,s^{-1}}$. How far from the centre of the landing zone does the motorcycle land?

d) In an effort to jump further the motorcyclist suggests that he could use a heavier, more powerful motorcycle. He is concerned that this heavier machine would 'drop more quickly'. What advice would you give to the motorcyclist?

6 Scalars and Vectors

1 Which of the following is a vector quantity?
   a) Energy
   b) Mass
   c) Power
   d) Acceleration
   e) Time

2 In a windsurfing event a competitor passes the first marker and travels 3 km due north towards the second marker. After passing the second marker the competitor sails 2.5 km north east towards the third marker.
   a) Calculate the distance travelled by the windsurfer between the first and third markers.
   b) By scale diagram or otherwise, determine the displacement of the third marker from the first marker.
   c) The windsurfer takes 45 minutes to complete the course.
      i) Calculate the average speed of the windsurfer.
      ii) Calculate the average velocity of the windsurfer between the first and third markers.

3 At the start of a yacht race one competitor expects to arrive at a position 20 km due north in 11 hours. During the 11 hours sailing time the yacht is blown 3 km to the east of the anticipated finishing position.
   a) Calculate the yacht's displacement at the end of the 11 hours.
   b) Calculate the average velocity of the yacht.
   c) What course should the yacht have taken so as to arrive 20 km due north of the starting position 11 hours after the beginning of the race? (You should assume that the speed of the yacht is the same as you calculated in part a).

4 Forces of 100 N and 35 N act on a point as shown in Figure 6.1.
   a) Calculate the resultant of these two forces.
   b) Another force of 40 N is added in the direction shown in Figure 6.2.

      What effect does this force have on the resultant of the other two? Explain your answer.

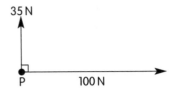

Figure 6.1

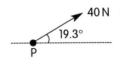

Figure 6.2

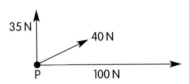

Figure 6.3

   c) What is the resultant of the three forces acting on the point shown in Figure 6.3? Explain your answer.

5 A force of 500 N acts at an angle of 35° to the horizontal.
   a) Calculate the component of this force in the horizontal direction.
   b) Calculate the component of this force in the vertical direction.

6 Figure 6.4 shows a diagram taken from an amateur pilot's handbook. The pilot wants to plot a course due east but has to take account of a steady wind blowing *from* the northwest.
   a) Explain why the bearing that the pilot must fly on is less than 090.
   b) In the first part of the journey the wind speed is 3.5 m s^{-1} while the plane is flying at 35 m s^{-1}.
      i) Calculate the bearing on which the pilot must fly for the plane to travel due east.
      ii) Calculate the velocity of the plane as seen by an observer on the ground.

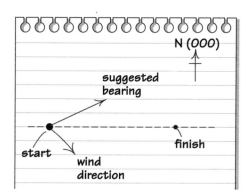

Figure 6.4

c) In the later part of the journey the wind speed drops. Describe and explain TWO changes that the pilot could make in order to arrive at his destination.

7 A weather station releases a balloon that rises at a constant speed of $15\,\mathrm{m\,s^{-1}}$. There is a wind blowing *towards* due west at a speed of $6.5\,\mathrm{m\,s^{-1}}$.

a) Calculate the magnitude and direction of the velocity of the balloon.

b) i) Calculate the time taken for the balloon to reach a height of $3000\,\mathrm{m}$ vertically above the ground.

ii) Calculate the horizontal displacement of the balloon when it is $3000\,\mathrm{m}$ vertically above the ground.

7   Newton's Laws

1 A student writes the following statement in her notebook. Certain words have been left out.

Copy this sentence and add one word in each of the spaces so that the sentence describes the effects that forces can have on an object.

A force acting on an object can change either the ... of the object, the ... at which the object is moving or the ... in which the object is moving.

2 A student writes the following statements in his notebook:

A: *When a block of wood is pushed along a level desk and released it comes to rest because of the frictional forces.*

B: *When a vehicle on a frictionless surface is pushed with a constant force it accelerates.*

C: *When an object moves along a horizontal surface the forces in the vertical plane are balanced.*

a) For each case draw a force diagram showing the important forces which are acting.

b) What would have to be done to the block in A if it is to take a longer time to come to rest?

c) An aeroplane is travelling horizontally in order to take off. Describe how the vertical forces on the aeroplane change as it accelerates along the horizontal runway.

3 Figure 7.1 shows a picture of a tent attached by guy ropes to tent pegs.

Figure 7.1

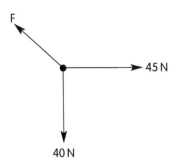

Figure 7.2

A student attempting to analyse the forces acting on a tent peg draws the diagram shown in Figure 7.2.

a) State the magnitude and direction of the force marked F on Figure 7.2.

b) What is the size of the horizontal component of this force?

4 A hot air balloon is ascending vertically at a speed of $1 \, m \, s^{-1}$. A sky-diver drops over the side of the balloon's basket which is 1500 m above the ground.

a) Explain why the sky-diver still ascends momentarily after dropping over the side of the balloon's basket.

b) During the next few seconds the sky-diver falls faster and faster, before reaching her terminal velocity.

  i) Describe how the forces on the sky-diver alter during the time she accelerates until she reaches terminal velocity.

  ii) As she approaches the ground she decelerates by opening her parachute. Describe how the forces on her alter as she slows down.

5 Air is removed from a long wide tube. A table tennis ball is filled with air while another is filled with water. The table tennis balls are dropped, simultaneously, from the same height in the tube.

a) Explain why both balls hit the bottom of the tube at the same time.

b) Air is now returned to the tube. The balls are again dropped simultaneously. Which ball reaches its terminal velocity first? Explain your answer.

6 A dragster with a mass of 870 kg accelerates from rest to a speed of 29 m s^{-1} in 0.61 s.

   a) Calculate the average acceleration of the dragster.

   b) Calculate the average force acting on the dragster as it accelerates.

   c) The driver of the dragster has a mass of 70 kg. Calculate the force needed to accelerate the driver as he sits in his seat for the 0.61 s of the run.

   d) Calculate the time taken for the dragster to travel the 400 m length of track.

7 A swimmer of mass 64 kg drops, from rest, from a board 3 m above a swimming pool.

   a) Calculate the speed of the swimmer as he enters the water.

   b) The swimmer comes to rest 0.8 m below the surface of the pool. Calculate the average force exerted by the water on the swimmer.

8 Newton 2

1 A car accelerates uniformly from rest and travels 40 m in 3 s.
   a) Calculate the acceleration of the car.
   b) The car has a mass of 720 kg. Calculate the unbalanced force needed to produce this acceleration.

2 A student investigating the magnitude of frictional force sets up the apparatus shown in Figure 8.1. The student uses a motion sensor connected to a computer to obtain a velocity–time graph for the motion of the trolley as it moves along the runway.

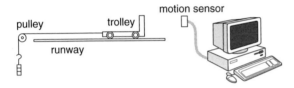

Figure 8.1

   a) Sketch the type of velocity–time graph that the student would expect to record if the trolley is moving at a constant velocity.
   b) With a towing force of 0.15 N, the trolley moves at a steady speed along an apparently smooth runway. What is the value of the frictional force between the runway and the trolley? Explain your answer.
   c) The towing force is now increased to 0.85 N.
      i) Calculate the unbalanced force acting on the trolley.
      ii) Sketch, on your velocity–time graph from your answer to a), the type of graph that the student would now expect.
   d) The runway is covered with a rougher material. Explain the type of evidence that the student would now have to collect to prove that the frictional forces in this situation were greater.

3 A textbook contains the following passage from which some of the numbers have been omitted.

   When a mass of 1 kg is falling freely the pull of the earth causes it to accelerate at ... m s⁻². According to Newton's second law we can say that a 1 kg mass accelerating at 9.8 m s⁻² is being pulled by an unbalanced force of ... N. If the same 1 kg mass is held stationary while attached to the end of a newton balance, the spring must be exerting an upwards force of ... N.

   a) Copy and complete the paragraph by adding the missing numbers.
   b) i) What is the acceleration of a 1.5 kg mass when falling freely towards the earth?
      ii) Calculate the unbalanced force acting on the 1.5 kg mass during freefall.
   c) A 1 kg mass and the 1.5 kg mass are released simultaneously to fall freely from the same height. Explain why they will land simultaneously.

4 During a Grand Prix a Formula 1 car of mass 1800 kg is travelling along a straight level road. The car has a velocity of $14\,\mathrm{m\,s^{-1}}$ when the brakes are applied. The car decelerates uniformly to rest after 3.62 s.

Figure 8.2

   a) Calculate the deceleration of the car.
   b) Calculate the distance travelled while the car is coming to rest.
   c) Calculate the average braking force.

5 A vertical take off aeroplane with a weight of 52 500 N lifts off from the deck of an aircraft carrier. The aeroplane has a vertical acceleration of $2\,\mathrm{m\,s^{-2}}$.
   a) Calculate the unbalanced upwards force needed to produce the acceleration.

Figure 8.3

b) Draw a force diagram to show the weight of the aeroplane and the thrust produced by the engines.

c) Calculate the size of the thrust produced by the engines at take off.

d) On the return journey to the aircraft carrier the weight of the plane has reduced to 50 000 N. The plane is descending at 3 m s⁻¹ when it is 18 m above the deck.

   i) Calculate the deceleration required to bring the plane smoothly to rest on the deck of the ship.

   ii) Calculate the time taken for the plane to land.

   iii) Calculate the thrust that the engines of the plane must produce to ensure that it lands smoothly on the deck of the ship.

6 A steel rope can exert a maximum force of 100 000 N before it will break. This rope is used in the type of simple crane shown in Figure 8.4.

a) What size of upwards force must the rope exert to lift the a mass of 4500 kg at a

Figure 8.4

constant speed of 0.75 m s⁻¹? Explain your answer.

b) What is the maximum unbalanced upward force that the rope can exert on the 4500 kg mass?

c) Calculate the maximum acceleration that the rope can give to the 4500 kg mass.

7 As a cricket ball with a mass of 450 g is caught, its speed reduces from 25 m s⁻¹ to rest in 5 ms.

Figure 8.5

a) Calculate the deceleration of the ball as it is caught.

b) Draw a diagram to show the direction in which the ball is moving and the magnitude and direction of the force acting on the ball as it is caught.

c) Draw a diagram to show the magnitude and direction of the force acting on the fielder as the ball is caught.

8 The vehicle on the air track shown in Figure 8.6 is pulled by a falling mass of 0.2 kg. The mass of the air track vehicle is 1.1 kg.

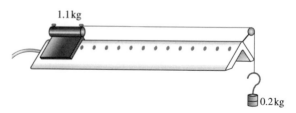

Figure 8.6

a) Show, by calculation, that the air track vehicle and the falling mass both accelerate at 1.51 m s⁻².

b) What pulling force is required to make the air track vehicle accelerate at 1.51 m s⁻²?

c) Copy and complete Figure 8.7 to show the forces acting on the air track vehicle as it accelerates at $1.51 \, \mathrm{m \, s^{-2}}$.

for vehicle

unbalanced force = _____ N

Figure 8.7

d) Show that the pulling force required to make the falling mass accelerate at $1.51 \, \mathrm{m \, s^{-1}}$ is $0.3 \, \mathrm{N}$.

for falling mass

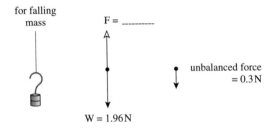

$F = $ _____

unbalanced force $= 0.3 \, \mathrm{N}$

$W = 1.96 \, \mathrm{N}$

Figure 8.8

e) A student analysing this situation draws the diagram shown in Figure 8.8. Copy and complete Figure 8.8 to show the forces acting on the falling mass as it accelerates.

f) Copy and complete the following paragraph to describe the forces acting on the air track and falling mass system.

In this system the falling mass exerts a ... N pulling force on the air track vehicle. The air track vehicle exerts a force of ... N on the falling mass. The force of the falling mass on the air track vehicle is ... in magnitude but acts in a direction ... to the force from the vehicle on the mass.

9 Impulse and Momentum

1 A constant force of 50 N is applied to a 0.15 kg ball, which is initially at rest. The force is applied for 9 ms. Calculate:
   a) the size of the impulse applied to the ball,
   b) the change in momentum of the ball,
   c) the velocity of the ball immediately after the force is removed.

2 A car with a mass of 740 kg is accelerated uniformly from $0\,\mathrm{m\,s^{-1}}$ to $10\,\mathrm{m\,s^{-1}}$ in 4 s.
   a) Calculate the acceleration of the car.
   b) Calculate the force required to produce this acceleration.
   c) Calculate the change in momentum of the car.
   d) Show, by calculation, that the impulse provided by the car's engine is numerically equal to the change in the car's momentum.

3 As a baseball is being caught its speed reduces from $25\,\mathrm{m\,s^{-1}}$ to rest in 5 ms. The mass of the baseball is 0.15 kg.
   a) Calculate the average deceleration of the ball.
   b) What is the magnitude and direction of the force acting on the ball as it is caught?
   c) Draw a diagram to show the magnitude and direction of the force acting on the fielder who caught the ball.

4 A student analysing the force between a ball and a bat during an impact draws the force–time graph shown in Figure 9.1.
   a) What is the maximum force exerted on the ball during the impact?

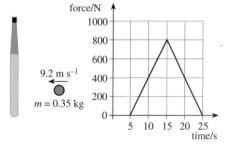

Figure 9.1

b) Calculate the impulse of the force from the bat on the ball during the impact.
c) What is the change in momentum of the ball?
d) Calculate the velocity of the ball immediately after the impact.

5 A car of mass 725 kg is moving at a constant speed of $18\,\mathrm{m\,s^{-1}}$ when a force is applied as shown in Figure 9.2. The force acts in the direction in which the car is moving.

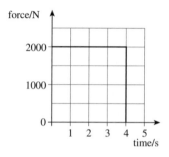

Figure 9.2

a) Calculate the velocity of the car immediately after the force is removed.
b) In another test the car is again travelling at $18\,\mathrm{m\,s^{-1}}$ and a force is applied as shown in Figure 9.3. Calculate the velocity of the car immediately after this force is removed.

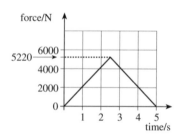

Figure 9.3

c) Draw a force–time graph to show how the car travelling at $18\,\mathrm{m\,s^{-1}}$ could be brought to rest in 5 s by a force of 2610 N. Explain your answer.

6 A ball of mass 0.35 kg is held stationary underneath a motion sensor. The ball is released and its velocity is measured at various points during the motion. The data is plotted on a graph as shown in Figure 9.4.

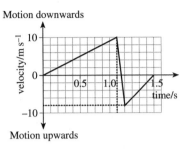

Figure 9.4

a) What is the velocity of the ball just before it hits the floor?

b) Approximately how far is the ball above the floor when it is released?

c) Calculate the momentum of the ball just before it hits the floor.

d) Calculate the momentum of the ball just as it loses contact with the floor after the first bounce.

e) Calculate the change in momentum during the first bounce.

f) Calculate the average resultant force that acts during the first bounce.

7 A pupil trying to analyse the forces acting while he is skateboarding draws the force–time graph shown in Figure 9.5. The pupil is initially standing at rest with one foot on the skateboard and the other in contact with the ground. The pupil and the skateboard have a combined mass of 60 kg. During the first second he pushes forward with a steady unbalanced force of 60 N.

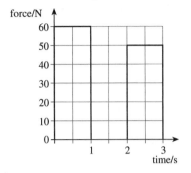

Figure 9.5

a) Calculate the average acceleration of the skateboarder during the first second.

b) Calculate the speed of the skateboarder 0.5 s after the start of the motion.

c) Calculate the speed of the skateboarder 1.5 s after the start of the motion.

d) From time $t = 1$ to $t = 2$ s he has both feet on the board and is moving at a constant speed. During the next second he again pushes on the ground but with a steady force of 50 N. Calculate his speed 3 s after the start of the motion.

e) Draw a speed–time graph for the skateboarder during the 3 s of the motion.

10 Conservation of Momentum

1 Vehicles A and B, of mass 0.8 kg and 0.6 kg respectively, travel towards each other and collide on an air track.

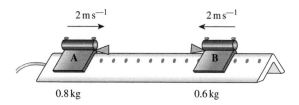

Figure 10.1

The velocities of the vehicles are as shown in Figure 10.1.
a) Calculate the momentum of vehicle A before the collision.
b) Calculate the momentum of vehicle B before the collision.
c) After the collision vehicle A continues to the right with a speed of $0.2 \, \text{m s}^{-1}$. Calculate the velocity of vehicle B after the collision.

2 A ball of mass 0.05 kg is fired horizontally from a projectile launcher which is at rest on a frictionless track. The ball leaves the launcher with a speed of $8.3 \, \text{m s}^{-1}$.

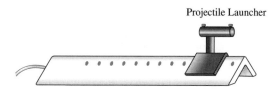

Projectile Launcher

Figure 10.2

a) State the Law of Conservation of Momentum.
b) Calculate the momentum of the ball as it leaves the launcher.
c) What is the momentum of the launcher after the ball is fired?
d) The projectile launcher has a mass of 1.75 kg. Calculate the recoil velocity of the launcher.

3 A spacecraft travelling at $100 \, \text{m s}^{-1}$ is made up from two separate stages which are initially joined together. The total mass of both stages is 7000 kg.
a) Calculate the momentum of the spacecraft as it travels through space.
b) At a predetermined time the craft separates into two parts. The smaller front stage has a mass of 1000 kg. Immediately after separation the smaller stage moves with a speed of $170 \, \text{m s}^{-1}$ directly away from the other stage.
   i) Calculate the momentum of the smaller stage of the spacecraft after separation.
   ii) What is the momentum of the larger stage of the spacecraft after separation? Explain your answer.
   iii) Calculate the speed of the larger stage of the spacecraft after separation.

4 A steel ball with a mass of 0.20 kg is dropped from a height of 0.46 m on to a stretched elastic sheet.
a) Calculate the speed of the ball just before it hits the elastic sheet.
b) Calculate the momentum of the ball just before it hits the elastic sheet.
c) The ball rebounds to a height of 0.32 m. Show that the ball rebounds from the elastic sheet with an upward velocity of $2.5 \, \text{m s}^{-1}$.
d) Calculate the change in momentum of the ball while it is in contact with the elastic sheet.

5 A car of mass 875 kg accelerates from $10 \, \text{m s}^{-1}$ to $44 \, \text{m s}^{-1}$ in 70 s.
a) Calculate the momentum of the car before it accelerates.
b) Calculate the change in the momentum of the car as a result of the acceleration.
c) What is the impulse of the force required to cause this change in momentum? Explain your answer.
d) Calculate the magnitude of the force required to produce this impulse.

6 During an ice hockey game the player controlling the puck is moving towards goal with a speed of $10 \, \text{m s}^{-1}$. He hits the puck by applying a horizontal force of 45 N for 0.14 s. The puck has a mass of 0.145 kg.

Figure 10.3

a) The puck is moving with a speed of $10\,\mathrm{m\,s^{-1}}$ just before it is hit. Calculate the momentum of the puck before the player takes the shot at goal.

b) Calculate the impulse of the force of the shot.

c) What is the change in momentum of the puck as a result of the shot? Explain your answer.

d) Calculate the speed of the puck just after contact with the stick.

7 A student sets up the apparatus in Figure 10.4 to estimate the force exerted on a football when it is kicked. The mass of the ball is 0.62 kg.

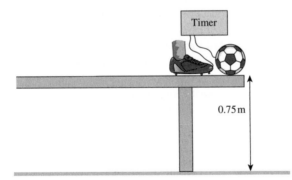

Figure 10.4

a) In an initial test the ball is dropped over the edge of the bench. Calculate the time that the ball takes to fall to the ground.

b) The ball is now kicked horizontally from a bench 0.75 m above the ground. The timer measures a time of contact of 57 ms between the toe of the boot and the ball. The ball hits the ground 2.5 m from the base of the table.

i) The student states that when the ball is kicked horizontally it takes the same time to hit the ground as when it is dropped vertically from the same height. Comment on this statement.

ii) Show that the ball takes 0.39 s to hit the ground

iii) Calculate the horizontal velocity of the ball as it leaves the table.

iv) Calculate the average force on the ball as it is kicked.

c) The student attempts to explain how the contact force varies with time by drawing the diagrams shown in Figures 10.5 and 10.6. What feature of these two diagrams must be the same? Explain your answer.

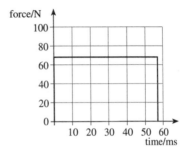

Figure 10.5

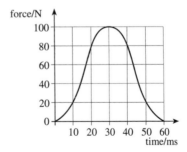

Figure 10.6

11 Energy, Work and Power

1 A workman pushes a 35 kg mass a distance of 10 m across a horizontal floor at a steady speed by applying a pushing force of 950 N. Calculate the work done.

2 A delivery van driver is required to deliver a washing machine of mass 48 kg to a third floor flat which is 28 m above ground level.
   a) Calculate the minimum work done by the delivery man in carrying the washing machine up the stairs.
   b) It takes the delivery man 4 minutes and 10 seconds to climb the stairs. Calculate the average minimum power.

3 A pendulum with a mass of 0.2 kg is pulled to one side as shown in Figure 11.1. The 0.2 kg mass is 5 cm vertically above its rest position.

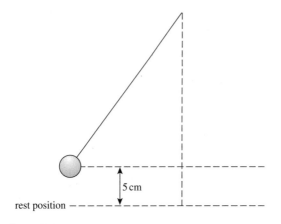

5 cm

rest position

Figure 11.1

a) Calculate the potential energy of the mass in this position.
b) Show, by calculation that, when released, the pendulum will pass through its rest position with a speed of 0.99 m s^{-1}.
c) The same pendulum is used in the apparatus shown in Figure 11.2
   i) Calculate the kinetic energy of the pendulum just before it hits the stationary mass.
   ii) The stationary 0.3 kg mass moves off with a speed of 0.75 m s^{-1}. State whether the collision is elastic. Justify your answer.

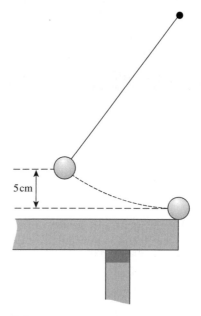

5 cm

Figure 11.2

4 A 0.95 kg trolley is released from the top of a slope and allowed to bounce off a bumper at the other end of the slope. A student uses a motion sensor to record the velocity–time graph for the trolley.
   a) Calculate the kinetic energy of the trolley just before it hits the bumper.
   b) i) Determine the speed of the trolley just after its impact with the bumper. Explain your answer.

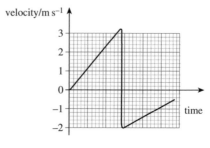

velocity/m s^{-1}

time

Figure 11.3

ii) Calculate the kinetic energy of the trolley just after its impact with the bumper.

iii) Show, by calculation, that the collision is inelastic.

5 Which row in the following table shows the correct units for power and work?

	Power	Work
A	$J\,s$	$J\,s^{-1}$
B	$J^{-1}\,s$	W
C	W^{-1}	J
D	W	J
E	W	J^{-1}

6 A car of mass 875 kg is brought to rest from a speed of $40\,\mathrm{m\,s^{-1}}$ in a distance of 25 m.

a) Calculate the kinetic energy of the car before the brakes are applied.

b) What is the work done in bringing the car to rest? Explain your answer.

c) Calculate the average braking force used to stop the car.

7 Which of the following correctly describes the kinetic energy and momentum before and after an elastic collision?

	Total momentum	Total kinetic energy
A	No Change	Decreased
B	Reduced	No Change
C	No Change	No Change
D	Increased	Reduced
E	No Change	Increased

8 In an experiment on collisions between vehicles on an air track, vehicle A is travelling at $4\,\mathrm{m\,s^{-1}}$ towards vehicle B which is at rest. Vehicle A has a mass of 0.39 kg and vehicle B has a mass of 0.25 kg.

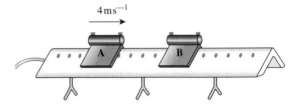

Figure 11.4

a) Calculate the kinetic energy of vehicle A before the collision.

b) During the collision the vehicles stick together.

i) Calculate the velocity of the vehicles just after the collision.

ii) Show by calculation that approximately 1.22 J of kinetic energy are transformed into other forms of energy during this collision.

9 A motor cruiser is travelling across a lake at a steady speed of $1.5\,\mathrm{m\,s^{-1}}$. The frictional forces resisting the motion are 2750 N.

a) What is the thrust produced by the engines on the motor cruiser? Explain your answer.

b) Calculate the work done by the engine against friction when the motor cruiser travels 30 m across the lake.

c) The boat's engine is 7.5% efficient. Calculate the total energy input needed by the engine for each 30 m travelled across the lake.

d) Calculate the power of the engine.

12 Weight and Mass

1 A student's notebook contains the following passages but some of the words have been omitted. Copy and complete these passages.

Any object near the surface of the Earth experiences a force of attraction pulling it towards the centre of the Earth. This force is called the . . . . If an object is dropped from the top of a tall building it will accelerate towards the centre of the Earth with an acceleration of . . . $m s^{-2}$. This acceleration is caused by the . . . acting as an unbalanced force.

Near the surface of the Earth the gravitational attraction between the Earth and a mass causes a force of attraction of approximately 9.8 N for each 1 kg of the object's mass. 9.8 $N kg^{-1}$ is described as the Earth's gravitational . . . . On the Moon a mass of 1 kg will have a weight of approximately 1.6 N. From this fact we can see that a mass freely falling towards the centre of the Moon will accelerate at . . . $m s^{-2}$.

2 The handle of a shopping bag breaks when a force of 250 N or greater is applied. Purchases with a mass of 20 kg are placed in the bag.
   a) Calculate the weight of the purchases in the bag.
   b) What unbalanced force can be used to lift the bag without the handles breaking? Explain your answer.
   c) Calculate the maximum acceleration of the bag when being lifted without the handle breaking.
   d) Show that the handle of the bag will break if it is lifted from the ground with an acceleration of 3 m s^{-2} or greater.

3 A group of students investigating unbalanced forces attach a 5 kg mass to a newton balance. The balance is attached to the roof of a lift which is stationary on the ground floor of a tall building.
   a) Confirm, by calculation, that the reading shown on the newton balance in the stationary lift is 49 N.
   b) As the lift travels upwards the students record the reading shown on the newton balance at regular intervals. Figure 12.1 shows the force–time graph for the motion.

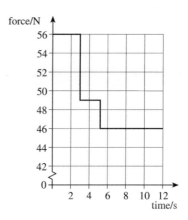

Figure 12.1

   i)   Draw a diagram to show the forces acting on the 5 kg mass during the first 3 s.
   ii) Calculate the upwards acceleration of the lift during the first 3 s of the motion.
   iii) Calculate the speed of the lift 3 s after the start of its acceleration.
   c) The force shown on the newton balance between time $t = 3$ s and $t = 5$ s is 49 N. Describe the motion of the lift during this time.
   d) Draw a diagram to show the forces acting on the 5 kg mass 7 s after the start.
   e) Calculate the deceleration needed for the lift to come to a stop 12 s after leaving the ground floor.
   f) Show that, at the end of its journey, the lift is 21.9 m above its starting position.

4 A helicopter of mass 3750 kg with its 750 kg payload attached ascends vertically with an acceleration of 2 m s^{-2}.

Figure 12.2

a) Calculate the weight of the helicopter and the payload.

b) Calculate the *unbalanced force* required to produce the acceleration.

c) Show, by calculation, that the lift force generated by the propellers of the helicopter is 53.1 kN.

d) The rope attaching the payload to the helicopter now breaks. The upward force on the helicopter from the rotor blades remains unaltered. Describe the motion of the helicopter. Include a calculation in your answer.

5 A laundry lift in a large hotel has a mass of 30 kg. Wet towels with a mass of 20 kg are placed on the lift which travels upwards through a height of 8 m in 16 s.

a) Calculate the combined weight of the lift and the towels.

b) Calculate the gravitational potential energy gained by the lift and the towels.

c) Calculate the average power delivered from the lift motor as it raises the wet towels.

13 Density and Pressure

1 A man with a mass of 76 kg wears shoes with an
  area of contact of 480 cm² with the ground.
  a) What is the weight of the man?
  b) Calculate the area in contact with the ground
     in m².
  c) Calculate the pressure exerted by the man on
     the ground.
  d) Describe, in words, how this pressure alters
     as the man walks forward.

2 Figure 13.1 shows the kind of diagram that is
  found in many junior physics textbooks.
  The ballerina of mass 56 kg stands on one stiletto
  heel of area 1 cm² while the elephant of mass
  2500 kg stands on four pads each of area 120 cm².
  a) Calculate the weight of the ballerina.
  b) Calculate the area of contact, in m², between
     the elephant and the ground.
  c) In which situation is the greatest pressure
     exerted on the ground? Justify your answer
     with a calculation.
  d) In which situation is the greatest force
     exerted on the ground?

Figure 13.1

3 A lab technician attempting to identify the liquid
  contents of an unmarked bottle pours a quantity
  of the liquid into a measuring cylinder.

  The following data is recorded for the liquid:
  mass of empty measuring cylinder = 102.53 g
  mass of cylinder + liquid = 223.09 g
  a) Use the data to calculate the volume of the
     liquid in the measuring cylinder.
  b) Calculate the density of the liquid.

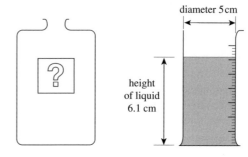

Figure 13.2

4 An engineer modelling the operation of a
  hydraulic braking system draws the diagram
  shown in Figure 13.3
  a) Calculate the area of the plunger in the
     master piston.
  b) The driver pushes the brake pedal so that it
     exerts a force of 250 N on the master piston.
     i)   Calculate the pressure that the driver
          exerts on the master piston.
     ii) What is the pressure exerted on the slave
          piston at each side of the large disc?
          Explain your answer.
     iii) Calculate the force exerted on the large
          disc by one of the pistons.

5 A platform of mass 250 kg floats in a tank of
  water at a large sealife centre. The platform is
  rectangular with sides 3 m × 4 m. The
  atmospheric pressure at sea level is 1 × 10⁵ Pa.
  a) Calculate the weight of the platform.
  b) Calculate the downwards force that the
     atmospheric pressure exerts on the platform.
  c) Calculate the upwards force exerted by the
     water on the floating platform.

6 Figure 13.4 shows apparatus used by a student
  to measure the density of air.

  When the valve is open the 1000 cm³ flask has a
  mass of 145.35 g. When the flask has been
  evacuated and the air tight valve shut, the flask
  has a mass of 144.17 g.
  a) Explain why there is a mass decrease when
     the flask is evacuated.
  b) Use the data given in the question to
     estimate the density of air. State one
     assumption that you have made.

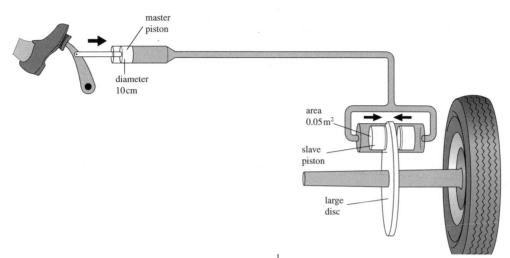

Figure 13.3

c) An accurate value for the density of air is quoted as $1.3\,\text{kg m}^{-3}$. By referring to this value comment on the accuracy of the student's results.

7 The air pressure in a car tyre is 2.1×10^5 Pa. The tyre makes contact with the road on a rectangular area of $10\,\text{cm} \times 17\,\text{cm}$. The car has a mass of 936 kg and its weight is distributed evenly by all four tyres.
   a) Calculate the weight of the car.
   b) Calculate the pressure exerted on the ground by one of the tyres.

8 When a block of ice is cooled from $0\,°\text{C}$ to $-4\,°\text{C}$ it expands due to an increase in the hydrogen bonding between the water molecules. Which ONE of the following statements is correct?
   A The density and the mass of the water decrease.
   B The density of the ice increases and its mass stays the same.
   C The volume of the ice increases and its density decreases.
   D The density and the mass are unaltered.
   E The mass remains constant and the density increases.

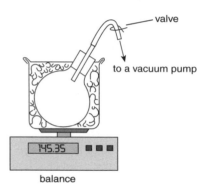

Figure 13.4

9 Which row in the following table shows the relative magnitudes of the interatomic spacing in solids, liquids and gases?

	Solids	Liquids	Gases
A	1	5	100
B	1	1	1
C	5	10	50
D	1	1	10
E	1	10	10

14 Pressure in Liquids and Gases

1 Figure 14.1 shows a diagram that is often found in textbooks.

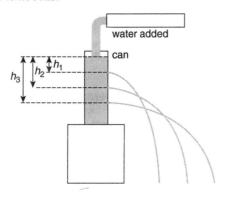

Figure 14.1

a) Explain why the jet of water from the lowest hole in the can squirts out the furthest.

b) The lowest hole in the can is 10 cm beneath the water level.

i) Calculate the pressure at this hole caused by the water alone. (Density of water 1000 kg m^{-3}.)

ii) Atmospheric pressure acting on the top of the water is 101 kPa. Calculate the total pressure acting at the lowest hole.

iii) The lowest hole has an area of 1 mm^2. With what force is the water pushed out of the hole?

2 The water pressure at the bottom of an ocean trench is 1.1×10^8 Pa. The pressure at the surface of the water is 101 kPa.

a) What percentage of the pressure at the bottom of the trench is caused by the atmospheric pressure acting on the surface?

b) Calculate the depth of the trench. You should assume that the density of water is 1000 kg m^{-3}.

c) Using another technique which she knows to be more accurate, an oceanographer measures the depth of the trench as 10 480 m. Explain why estimating the depth of the trench using the pressure measurement is likely to give a reading which is higher than the actual value.

3 An engineer designing a system for pressurising the cabin of a transatlantic aircraft starts by

recording the pressure outside the aircraft as it makes its descent from an altitude of 9500 m. The descent is in three stages.

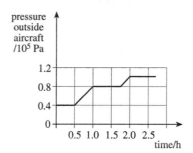

Figure 14.2

a) From the data given in the graph estimate the density of the air outside the aircraft at a height of 9500 m. (Assume that $g = 10$ m s^{-2}.)

b) Suggest a reason why the pressure in the aircraft's cabin is reduced when the aircraft is cruising at 9500 m.

c) Explain why the pressure in the cabin of the aircraft must be returned to 101 kPa before the aircraft lands.

4 A man of mass 79 kg is horizontal at a depth of 1.6 m in a swimming pool.

a) Calculate the weight of the man.

b) Calculate the total pressure acting at a depth of 1.6 m in water of density 1000 kg m^{-3}.

c) The pressure at any depth in a liquid acts in all directions. Explain why the man appears to be lighter when he is in the water.

5 An altimeter is used to indicate the height of an aircraft above sea level. One type of altimeter uses the fact that air pressure varies with height to give its reading.

a) State a mathematical relationship between pressure P and height h in a medium where the density is constant.

b) Figure 14.3 shows an altimeter where part of the linear scale is missing. Copy this diagram and complete the markings on the scale. (You should assume that at the heights where this altimeter are used the density of air and the gravitational field strength are constant.)

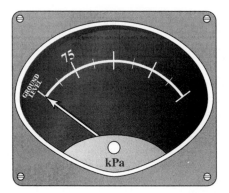

Figure 14.3

15 Flotation and Upthrust

Figure 15.1

1 A student attaches a block of mass 1 kg to a newton balance as shown in Figure 15.1.
   a) Calculate the weight of the block.
   b) The block is then immersed in a liquid and the reading on the newton balance reduces to 8.4 N.
      i)   Calculate the size of the buoyancy force produced by the water.
      ii) Explain, in words, the origin of this buoyancy force.
   c) The student reads in a textbook that the size of the buoyancy force is numerically the same as the weight of water displaced.

   What is the weight of water displaced by the block when it is immersed in the water? Explain your answer.

2 An object attached to a newton balance weighs 7.3 N. A pupil submerges the block in liquids X, Y and Z and obtains the readings shown in the following table:

X	Y	Z
6.0 N	6.4 N	5.3 N

   a) Which liquid exerts the greatest upthrust on the block? Explain your answer.
   b) Which of the three liquids has the lowest density? Explain your answer.

3 A large stone weighs 56 N. When the stone is placed in a tank of water of density 1030 kg m^{-3}, the water level on the side of the tank rises by 5.75 cm. This is shown in Figure 15.2.

stone

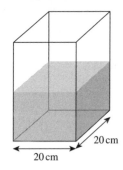

20 cm

20 cm

Figure 15.2

   a) Calculate the volume of water displaced when the stone is submerged. Explain your answer.
   b) Calculate the volume of the stone in m^3.
   c) Calculate the mass of water displaced by the submerged stone.
   d) What is the weight of water displaced by the submerged stone?
   e) Calculate the density of the stone.

4 A balloon is filled with helium of density 0.18 kg m^{-3} so that its volume is 0.18 m^3.
   a) Calculate the weight of air displaced by the balloon. You should assume that air has a density of 1.13 kg m^{-3}.
   b) The balloon and the helium it contains has a mass of 250 g. Calculate the weight of the balloon and its contents.
   c) Calculate the maximum mass that the balloon can lift in air.

5 A lead cube of side 10 cm weighs 157 N. This cube is now placed in water of density 1030 kg m^{-3}.
   a) Calculate the weight of water displaced by the lead cube.
   b) Show by calculation that the 'apparent weight' of the lead block is 147 N when placed in the water.
   c) Calculate the 'apparent weight' of the block when it is placed in oil of density 810 kg m^{-3}.

16 Gas Laws

1 Copy and complete the following statements connecting the pressure, temperature and volume of a fixed mass of gas.

The volume of a fixed mass of an ideal gas kept at constant temperature is ... proportional to the applied pressure. This law is called ... Law.

The pressure of a fixed mass of an ideal gas kept at constant volume is ... proportional to the ... temperature of the gas. This law is called ... Law.

The volume of a fixed mass of an ideal gas kept at constant pressure is .... proportional to the ... temperature of the gas.

2 Copy and complete the following table to show both the Celsius and Kelvin temperatures of the boiling and melting points indicated in the table.

	Celsius temperature)	Kelvin temperature
Boiling point of water	100	
Melting point of ice		273
Melting point of aluminium		932
Melting point of lead	327	
Boiling point of nitrogen	−196	
Boiling point of xenon		166

3 A cylinder containing xenon has a volume of $0.06\,m^3$. The pressure of the gas in the cylinder is 1.8 MPa.
  a) Calculate the volume that this mass of xenon would occupy at an atmospheric pressure of 101 kPa.
  b) Calculate the volume of xenon that will leave the cylinder when the tap is opened.
  c) A certain welding process uses this xenon to create an inert environment in a region where the atmospheric pressure is 101 kPa. In this process the xenon leaves the cylinder at a rate of $1000\,cm^3$ per minute. Calculate the time for which one cylinder will be able to sustain the inert environment.

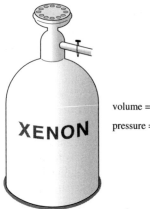

volume = $0.06\,m^3$

pressure = 1.8 MPa

Figure 16.1

4 A diver at the bottom of a 20 m deep pool of fresh water releases a small air bubble from his cylinder. The diver notices that the volume of the bubble increases as it rises towards the surface. The temperature of the water is constant at all depths while the density of the water is $1030\,kg\ m^{-3}$ and the surrounding atmospheric pressure is 101 kPa.

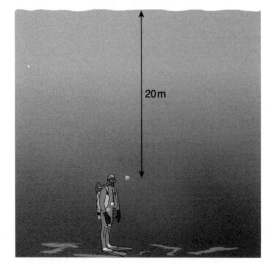

20 m

Figure 16.2

  a) Explain why the volume of the bubble increases as it rises towards the surface.
  b) The diver estimates that the volume of the bubble as it begins to rise is $2\,cm^3$. (You should assume that the pressure at the surface of the water is 101 000 Pa.)

i) Calculate the total pressure at the point where the bubble is released.

ii) Calculate the volume of the bubble when it reaches the surface.

5 A flask with a cork in it contains air at a pressure of 90 kPa and at a temperature of 27 °C. The flask is heated and the cork is forced out when the pressure of the air in the flask is 120 kPa.

a) Explain, in terms of the kinetic theory of gases, why the pressure increases when the flask is heated.

b) Calculate the temperature of the air in the flask when the cork is forced out.

c) With the flask still at this higher temperature the cork is reinserted and the flask is cooled to 27 °C. Explain why the cork in the flask is now more difficult to pull out.

6 Air with a volume of 6 cm³ and at a temperature of 23 °C is in a sealed syringe where the plunger is free to move.

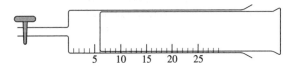

Figure 16.3

The pressure of the air in the syringe is initially 300 kPa. The pressure is reduced slowly to 100 kPa while the temperature of the gas is kept constant. The pressure and volume of the air change as shown in Figure 16.4.

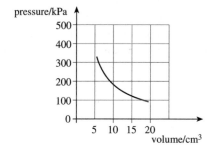

Figure 16.4

a) Show, by calculation, that the air occupies a volume of 18 cm³ at a pressure of 100 kPa.

b) The syringe is kept at a constant volume of 18 cm³ and heated until the pressure is 200 kPa.

i) Show, by calculation, that the temperature required to make the pressure 200 kPa is 592 K.

ii) Copy Figure 16.4 and complete it to include the process of heating the air, at constant volume, to make its pressure 200 kPa.

iii) Draw a line on Figure 16.4 to show how the pressure would alter when the volume of the air is reduced to 6 cm³ while its temperature is kept constant at 592 K.

17 Electric Fields

1 An electrically neutral polythene rod when rubbed with a woollen cloth becomes negatively charged. A cellulose acetate rod rubbed with a woollen rod becomes positively charged.

a) Explain, in terms of conservation of charge, how the polythene rod becomes negatively charged when rubbed.

b) Explain, in terms of conservation of charge, how the cellulose acetate rod becomes positively charged when rubbed with the woollen cloth.

2 Figure 17.1 shows a number of strands of artificial hair attached to the dome of a positively charged Van der Graaff generator.

Figure 17.1

a) Explain why the hair stands on end when the dome of the generator is charged.

b) Explain why the strands fall *slowly* when the generator is switched off.

3 Figure 17.2 shows a high voltage power supply connected to electrodes. The electrodes are dipped into a petri dish containing oil with small seeds sprinkled on the surface of the oil.

a) Draw a diagram to show the shape of the electric field produced in the oil.

b) The polarity of the electrodes is now reversed. Draw another diagram to show the new electric field. Describe the differences between this field and that in part a).

c) Describe how the apparatus could be altered to produce a parallel field between electrodes.

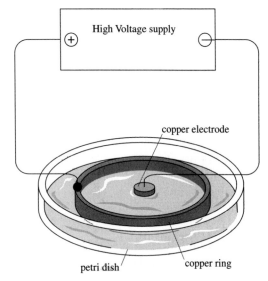

Figure 17.2

4 A textbook has the following diagram and description of an electrostatic smoke precipitator.

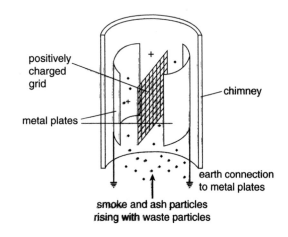

Figure 17.3

Copy and complete the following passage to describe how the precipitator reduces the quantity of flue ash discharged from a power station into the environment.

As the flue gases with particles of ash rise up the chimney, a central ... ionises the air molecules. These charged air molecules attach themselves to the electrically ... ash particles. The ash particles are now ... charged and are attracted to the earthed lining of the chimney. There is an electric field produced between the positively charged central electrode and the lining of the chimney. By collecting ash particles on the sides of the chimney, the quantity of ash discharged into the atmosphere is reduced.

18 Current, Voltage and Resistance

1 In the circuit of Figure 18.1 there is a current of 2.5 A for 2 minutes.

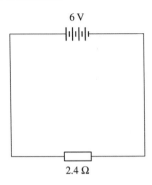

6 V

2.4 Ω

Figure 18.1

a) Calculate the quantity of charge which passes through the resistor in the 2 minutes.

b) The p.d. across the resistor is 6 V.
   i) How much energy is supplied to each coulomb of charge that passes through the resistor? Explain your answer.
   ii) Calculate the total quantity of energy passing through the resistor during the 2 minutes.

c) Explain why the temperature of the resistor increases.

2 In a chemistry electrolysis experiment, two electrodes are dipped into a solution of copper sulphate. A current of 2 A is supplied to the solution for 10 minutes.

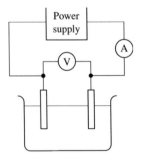

Power supply

V   A

Figure 18.2

a) Calculate the quantity of charge supplied to the solution by the current.

b) The size of the charge on an electron is 1.6×10^{-19} C. Calculate the number of electrons which pass into the solution during this electrolysis experiment.

3 An electron with a charge of -1.6×10^{-19} C is placed at rest between charged plates as shown in Figure 18.3. The p.d. between the plates is set to 1500 V.

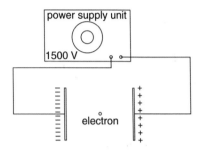

power supply unit

1500 V

electron

Figure 18.3

a) Explain why the electron accelerates as it moves between the plates.

b) Calculate the work done by the electric field on the electron as the electron moves between the plates.

c) How much kinetic energy does the electron gain in moving from the negative to the positive plate?

d) The electron is initially at rest. Calculate its speed just before it arrives at the positive plate. (The mass of the electron is 9.1×10^{-31} kg.)

4 In his famous experiment to investigate the charge on an oil drop, recreated in Figure 18.4, Millikan watched small droplets of oil falling vertically at a constant speed.

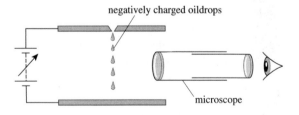

negatively charged oildrops

microscope

Figure 18.4

a) Draw a diagram to show the forces acting on a droplet as it falls vertically with a constant speed.

b) The droplet has a mass, m kg. What is the weight, in newtons, of the droplet?

c) The drop has a charge of q coulombs. What is the magnitude of the upwards force on the droplet?

d) Describe how the charge on the drop could be determined.

5 A student investigates how the current in a wire depends on the p.d. across the wire. The circuit used is shown below.

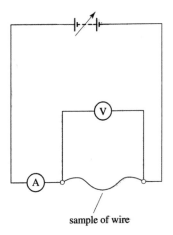

sample of wire

Figure 18.5

The student records the following pairs of p.d and current readings.

p.d./V	0	1.55	3.01	4.56	6.10
current/A	0	0.32	0.61	0.94	1.22

The student records the following description of these results in her notes:

As the p.d. across the wire ... the current in the wire ...

a) Copy and complete this statement to describe the trend illustrated by the student's results.

b) The student calculates the p.d. / current ratios for these results and notices that the ratios are approximately the same for each pair of results. What does this allow the student to conclude about the sample of wire used?

c) Draw a graph of p.d. (*y*-axis) versus current (*x*-axis) for the student's results.

d) From your graph determine the resistance of the sample tested.

e) The student notices that the wire begins to feel warm when the current in it exceeds 3 A. Explain the effect that this increase in temperature has on the resistance of wire.

6 The voltage–current characteristic for an LED shown in an electronics data sheet says that when the current in the LED is more than 2 mA the p.d. across the terminals of the LED remains constant at 1.5 V.

This LED is connected in series with a resistor as in Figure 18.6 and the current in the resistor is found to be 5 mA.

a) What is the current in the component? Explain your answer.

b) What is the p.d. across the component? Explain your answer.

c) Calculate the p.d. across the resistor.

d) Show that the resistor has a value of 1.5 kΩ.

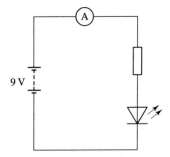

9 V

Figure 18.6

19 Series and Parallel Circuits

1 A student studying series circuits sets up the circuit as shown in Figure 19.1 The reading on ammeter A_1 is 0.25 A.

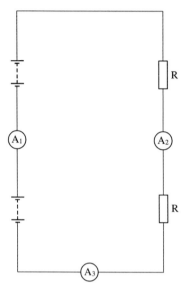

Figure 19.1

a) What are the readings on ammeters A_2 and A_3?

b) The student tries to summarise the behaviour of this circuit by recording the following comment in her notes. Copy and complete this statement to summarise the behaviour of the current in a series circuit.

The current in a series circuit is ... at all points in the circuit.

c) The student now connects a voltmeter in the circuit as shown in Figure 19.2. Voltmeters V_1 and V_2 both show readings of 4.5 volts. What is the reading recorded on voltmeter V_3?

d) The student again tries to summarise the behaviour of this circuit by recording the following comment in her notes. Copy and complete this statement to summarise the behaviour of the potential differences in a series circuit.

The ... of the p.d.s across the components in a series circuit equals the supply voltage.

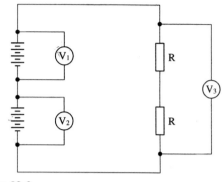

Figure 19.2

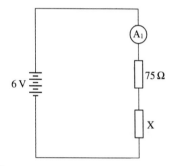

Figure 19.3

2 In the circuit shown in figure 19.3 the battery has no internal resistance. The current in the circuit is 20 mA.

a) Calculate the p.d. across the 75 Ω resistor.

b) What is the p.d. across resistor X? Explain your answer.

c) Calculate the resistance of resistor X.

d) What single value of resistor could be used to replace the two resistors in this circuit so that the current from the 6 V battery is still 20 mA? Explain your answer.

e) Resistor X and the 75 Ω resistor are now connected in parallel and connected to the 6 V battery as shown in Figure 19.4. Calculate the values of the currents at the points marked A_1, A_2 and A_3 in this circuit.

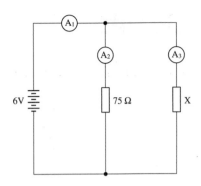

Figure 19.4

3 Resistors of resistance X, Y and Z are connected as shown in Figure 19.5.

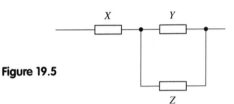

Figure 19.5

Which of **A** to **E** could be used to calculate the total resistance of this combination?

A $X + Y + Z$
B $X + (YZ/Y+Z)$
C $X - (YZ/Y+Z)$
D $X + (Y + Z)/YZ$
E $X + Y - Z$

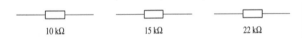

10 kΩ   15 kΩ   22 kΩ

Figure 19.6

4 An engineer designs a circuit using the resistors of resistance $10\,k\Omega$, $15\,k\Omega$ and $22\,k\Omega$.
   a) Show, by calculation, how two of these resistors could be connected to produce an effective resistance of $6\,k\Omega$.
   b) Determine the largest effective resistance that could be achieved with these three resistors.
   c) Show, by calculation, how all three of these resistors could be connected to produce an effective resistance of $28\,k\Omega$.
   d) Determine how the engineer could join these resistors to a 6 V battery, having negligible internal resistance, so that the current taken from the battery is 1.27 mA.

5 A student investigating electronic components sets up the test circuit shown in Figure 19.7. She is given three components labelled X, Y and Z. X and Y are resistors and Z is a lamp. She begins by testing component X, as in Figure 19.7, then repeats the same test with the other components.

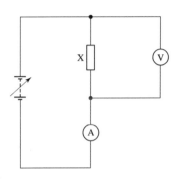

Figure 19.7

a) When testing the components she adjusts the power supply to obtain the pairs of voltage and current readings shown in the following tables. Plot these results on a *single* set of voltage (*y*-axis) and current axes.

Lamp Z

voltage/V	0	1	2	3	4
current/mA	0	30	42	50	56

Resistor X

voltage/V	0	1	2	3	4
current/mA	0	17	33	50	67

Resistor Y

voltage/V	0	1	2	3	4
current/mA	0	15	30	45	60

Figure 19.8

b) Resistors X and Y are now connected in parallel with the supply as shown in Figure 19.9. The p.d. of the output of the supply is set at 3.5 V.
   i)   What is the current in resistor X?
   ii) What is the current in resistor Y?
   iii) What is the current in the ammeter?
c) The student now connects resistor X and lamp Z in series, as shown in Figure 19.10. The reading recorded on the ammeter is 30 mA.

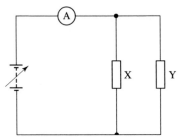

Figure 19.9

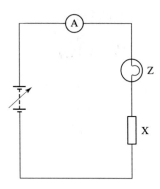

Figure 19.10

i)   What p.d. across resistor X will cause a current of 30 mA in the resistor?

ii) What p.d. across lamp Z will cause a current of 30 mA in lamp Z?

iii) Calculate the p.d. of the output of the supply needed to produce a current of 30 mA in the ammeter.

20 Voltage Dividers and Wheatstone Bridges

1 In the circuit shown in Figure 20.1 two resistors are connected in series with a 6 V power supply. The power supply has negligible internal resistance.

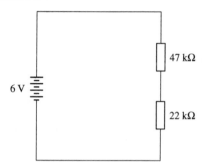

Figure 20.1

a) Calculate the effective value of the two resistors when connected in series.
b) Show, by calculation, that the current in each of the resistors is 87 μA.
c) Calculate the p.d. across the 47 kΩ resistor.
d) Show, by calculation, that the p.d. across the 22 kΩ resistor is 1.91 V.

2 In the circuit shown in Figure 20.2 resistors of value R_T and R_B are connected in series with a power supply which produces an output p.d. of V volts.

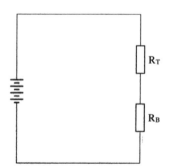

Figure 20.2

a) State the effective value of the two resistors.
b) Explain how the current in the circuit can be expressed as $V/(R_T + R_B)$.
c) Show that the p.d. V_{mp} across the resistor R_B can be expressed as
$$V_{mp} = \{R_B/(R_T + R_B)\} V$$

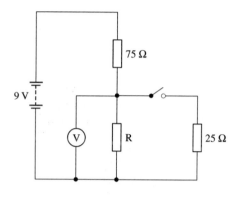

Figure 20.3

3 A pupil studying potential dividers sets up the circuit shown in Figure 20.3.
a) When the switch is open the voltmeter shows a reading of 3 V. What is the voltage across the 75 Ω resistor?
b) Calculate the current in the 75 Ω resistor when the switch is open.
c) Show, by calculation, that resistor R has a value of 37.5 Ω.
d) The student now closes the switch.
   i) Show, by calculation, that the resistors connected to the 9 V battery provide an effective resistance of 90 Ω.
   ii) Show by calculation that the p.d. across the 75 Ω resistor is 7.5 V.
   iii) Calculate the current in the 25 Ω resistor when the switch is closed.
e) When writing up her findings of this experiment, the student states that connecting the 25 Ω load resistor across the lower resistor in the potential divider reduces the voltage at the midpoint. Explain, using numerical values from the question, why this statement is correct.

4 A student sets up the Wheatstone Bridge circuit shown in Figure 20.4. The student adjusts the variable resistor until the bridge is balanced.
a) How would the student know when the bridge was balanced?
b) Calculate the resistance of the variable resistor required to balance the bridge.

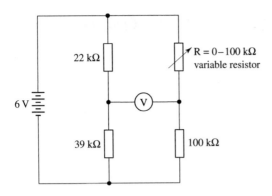

Figure 20.4

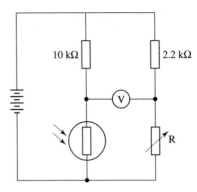

Figure 20.6

c) The student now connects another 39 kΩ resistor in parallel with the 39 kΩ resistor already in the bridge circuit. The student then finds that the bridge circuit will not balance. Explain why the bridge circuit will not balance.

d) Another student suggests that interchanging the positions of the 100 kΩ resistor and the variable resistor would allow the bridge to be balanced. Would you expect this change to allow the bridge to be balanced? Justify your answer with a calculation.

5 A student investigating the behaviour of a light dependent resistor finds that its resistances in bright daylight and darkness are 400 Ω and 100 kΩ respectively. The LDR is added into a circuit as shown in Figure 20.5. The battery has negligible internal resistance.

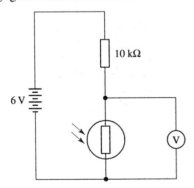

Figure 20.5

a) Show, by calculation, that the reading on the voltmeter will be 0.23 V when the LDR is in bright daylight.

b) Show, by calculation, that the reading on the voltmeter will be 5.45 V when the LDR is placed in darkness.

c) The LDR is now used as one of the resistors in the Wheatstone Bridge circuit shown in Figure 20.6.

   i) Calculate the value of resistance needed to balance the bridge when the LDR is placed in bright daylight.

   ii) Calculate the value of resistance needed to balance the bridge when the LDR is placed in darkness.

d) The LDR is placed in bright daylight and the variable resistor is adjusted until the bridge is balanced, as in Figure 20.7. The student then sets up a computerised system to record the output voltage from the bridge as the light level changes.

Sketch a graph to show how the p.d. across the Wheatstone Bridge changes as the resistance of the LDR varies.

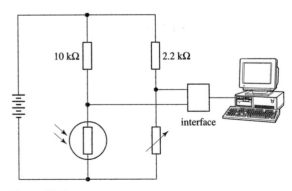

Figure 20.7

21 e.m.f. and Internal Resistance

1 Which of these statements correctly describes the e.m.f. of a power supply?

A The electrical potential energy supplied to each coulomb of charge passing through the supply.

B The energy wasted within a power supply when 1 coulomb of charge passes into an external circuit.

C The terminal p.d. when a current passes through a load resistor.

D Always less than the terminal p.d.

E The energy delivered by 1 coulomb of charge to a load resistor.

2 A student making notes about e.m.f. and internal resistance records the following three points:

I A very high resistance voltmeter across the terminals of a power supply will record the e.m.f. of the supply.

II The internal resistance of a battery can be calculated if the e.m.f. and short circuit current for the supply are known.

III The sum of the e.m.f.s around a closed circuit equals the sum of the p.d.s around the closed circuit.

Which of these statements are correct?

A I only

B II only

C I and II only

D II and III only

E I and II and III.

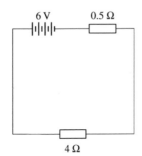

Figure 21.1

3 In the circuit shown in Figure 21.1 a battery with an e.m.f. of 6 V and internal resistance of 0.5 Ω is connected to a 4 Ω load resistor.

a) Calculate the current in the circuit.

b) Calculate the 'voltage lost' due to the internal resistance.

c) Show, by calculation, that the terminal p.d. for the battery is 5.33 V.

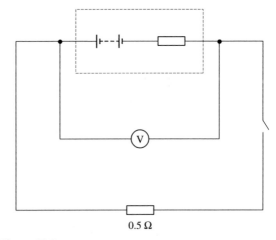

Figure 21.2

4 A very high resistance digital voltmeter connected across the terminals of a heavy duty lorry battery shows a reading of 24 V. When the battery is tested by supplying current to a 0.5 Ω load resistor the voltmeter reading falls to 22 V.

a) What is the e.m.f. of the battery? Explain your answer.

b) Calculate the current in the 0.5 Ω load resistor during the testing of the battery.

c) Show that the power dissipated in the load resistor during the battery testing is 968 W.

d) Show that the battery has an internal resistance of 0.045 Ω.

5 Four identical eells each of e.m.f. 1.5 V and internal resistance 0.3 Ω are connected in series to make a battery.

a) What is the maximum e.m.f. that the battery can supply? Explain your answer.

b) What is the total internal resistance of the 6 V battery? Explain your answer.

c) Calculate the initial current produced if the battery is accidentally short-circuited.

6 A student investigating internal resistance sets up the circuit shown in Figure 21.3. She records several pairs of current and terminal

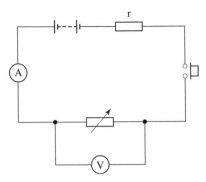

Figure 21.3

current/A	2	2.25	2.57	3	3.6	4.5
terminal p.d./V	6	5.6	5.14	4.5	3.6	2.25

Figure 21.4

p.d. readings for different settings of the variable resistor.

a) Draw a graph of terminal p.d. (*y*-axis) versus current (*x*-axis) for her readings. The terminal p.d. axis should be in the range 0–10 volts and the current axis should show values up to 7.5 A.

b) From your graph determine:
   i)   the e.m.f. of the battery
   ii) the short circuit current.

c) Calculate the internal resistance of the supply.

d) Calculate the power dissipated in the variable resistor for each of the pairs of readings in the table.

e) While researching this experiment the student reads the following passage in an advanced textbook:

The power delivered to a load resistor maximises when the value of the load resistor is equal to the internal resistance of the power supply.

i)   Using the values in the results table, determine the load resistances and plot a graph of power versus load resistance.

ii) Explain how your graph supports the passage which the student read in the textbook.

22 Electrical Energy and Power

1 A student investigating the heating of water estimates that it will take 174 kJ of energy to heat a beaker of water from 17 °C to 100 °C. She then uses a heater rated at 1 kW to warm the water in the beaker and she finds that it takes 3 minutes for the water to reach its boiling point.
   a) Show, by calculation, that the heater supplies 180 kJ of energy in 3 minutes.
   b) Explain why the quantity of energy required exceeds the student's estimate.

2 A small indicator lamp on an instrument control panel is rated 3.5 V and 250 mA. This lamp is connected in series with a resistor and joined to a 9 V power supply of negligible internal resistance.

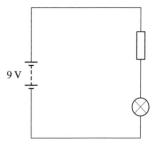

Figure 22.1

   a) What is the p.d. across the resistor when the indicator lamp is working at normal brightness? Explain your answer.
   b) Show that the series resistor should have a value of 22 Ω for the lamp to light at normal brightness.
   c) Calculate the power dissipated in the resistor.
   d) Calculate the quantity of electrical energy converted to other forms of energy by the lamp in 10 seconds.

3 a) Explain the purpose of a fuse in an electrical circuit.
   b) A 3 kW heater is connected to the 230 V domestic electricity supply. Calculate the current in the circuit.
   c) The heater in a domestic shower unit is rated at 9 kW.
      i) Calculate the current in the heater when the shower is operating.
      ii) Explain why the shower unit could not be powered using a circuit having a 13 A fuse.

4 A resistance substitution box is connected to a 9V battery pack which has an internal resistance of 2.5 Ω.

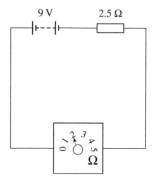

Figure 22.2

The value of the resistance box is set to 2 Ω.
   a) Show, by calculation, that the current in the 2 Ω resistor is 2 A.
   b) Calculate the power dissipated in the 2 Ω resistor.
   c) Calculate the quantity of electrical energy converted to heat by the internal resistance in 10 seconds.
   d) Determine the total quantity of electrical energy delivered by the battery in 10 s.

5 Figure 22.3 shows apparatus that can be used to demonstrate the advantages of power transmission systems using alternating rather than direct current. The wire used as the transmission line has a resistance of 1.5 Ω/m and the total length of the transmission line is 4.2 m. The lamp has a resistance of 11.5 Ω.

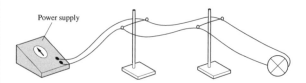

Power supply

Figure 22.3

a) Show by calculation that the total resistance of the transmission line is 6.3 Ω.

Figure 22.4 shows a student's attempt to explain how the transmission lines supply energy to the lamp.

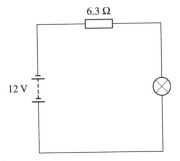

Figure 22.4

The e.m.f. of the d.c. power supply is 12 V and it has negligible internal resistance.

b) Calculate the current in the lamp.

c) Show, by calculation, that the power dissipated in the lamp is 5.2 W.

d) Show, by calculation, that the power dissipated in the transmission lines is 2.86 W.

e) What percentage of the total power produced by the power supply is converted into heat and light by the lamp?

f) A textbook states that for power distribution systems using alternating current, over 99% of the input energy is transferred to the user. Explain why it is advantageous to have a highly efficient power distribution system.

23 A.C. and R.M.S. Values

1 a) State the relationship between the peak and r.m.s. values for a sinusoidally varying alternating voltage.

b) The signal shown in Figure 23.1 has a peak value of 14 V. Calculate the r.m.s. value of this a.c. signal.

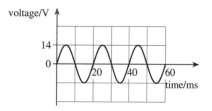

Figure 23.1

c) The frequency of the signal is doubled. Copy Figure 23.1 and add a trace to show how the new signal would compare with the original one.

2 With the apparatus in Figure 23.2 the lamp is lit from the 6 V d.c. supply when the switch is in the position shown. The brightness of the lamp is noted. The switch is now moved so that the lamp is supplied from the a.c. power supply.

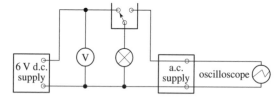

Figure 23.2

Calculate the peak value of the a.c. voltage that will result in the lamp emitting the same quantity of light as it did when connected to the d.c. supply.

3 An alternating voltage with a peak of 9 V is connected in series with a 1 kΩ resistor and an ammeter, as shown in Figure 23.3.
a) Calculate the r.m.s. current in the circuit.
b) Calculate the power dissipated in the resistor.

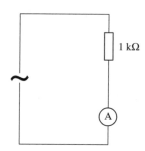

Figure 23.3

c) Another 1 kΩ resistor is now connected in parallel with the first one.
   i) Calculate the effective resistance of the resistors in parallel.
   ii) Calculate the new current in the circuit.
d) The a.c. supply is replaced with a battery and the ammeter is switched to measure direct current. Calculate the value of the voltage required for the d.c. supply to produce the same power dissipation in the parallel resistors.

4 A 6 V, 0.15 A lamp is connected to a 6 V battery of negligible internal resistance. The ammeter in the circuit indicates that the current in the lamp is 0.15 A. The p.d. of 6 V and the current of 0.15 A are described as the optimal operating conditions for the lamp.

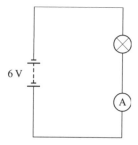

Figure 23.4

a) Show that the filament of the lamp has a resistance of 40 Ω.
b) Show that the power dissipated by the lamp lit at normal brightness is 900 mW.
c) The 6 V battery is now replaced with an a.c supply providing an r.m.s. output voltage of 6 V.

i) Calculate the peak output p.d. of the a.c. supply.

ii) Show that the peak current in the filament of the lamp is 0.21 A.

iii) Calculate the peak power dissipated by the filament of the lamp when connected to the a.c. supply.

iv) What is the average power dissipated by the filament of the lamp? Explain your answer.

v) A student suggests that the filament of the lamp will melt quicker with the a.c. supply than with the d.c. supply because for a short part of the cycle the power dissipated in the filament exceeds the optimum operating power.

Use some of the answers that you have calculated in this question to explain why this student's suggestion is correct.

24 Sensors, Transistors and Basic Electronics

1 A student making notes on elementary electronics records the following sentences. Some of the words have been omitted from these sentences. Copy and complete the sentences.

  a) *The output p.d. generated by a circuit sensing light can have any value between certain maximum and minimum values. This type of signal is called an ... signal.*

  b) *When a barcode is swiped across a barcode reader the electronic circuitry produces an output signal that is a mixture of high and low level segments. There are no values of the output between the high and low levels. This type of signal is called a ... signal.*

  c) *A solar cell converts some of the Sun's energy into ... energy.*

  d) *A thermocouple converts ... energy into electrical energy.*

  e) *If the output from a loudspeaker connected to an amplifier is to sound identical to the input, the frequency ... of the output must be the same as the input.*

2 An LED is designed to operate under optimum conditions with a p.d. of 3V across it and a current of 10 mA in it. The LED is to be powered from a 5 V power supply. A student suggests that a current limiting resistor must be put in series with the LED.

  a) What is the p.d. across the LED when it is operating under optimum conditions? Explain your answer.

  b) Calculate the p.d. across the current limiting resistor when the LED is operating under optimum conditions.

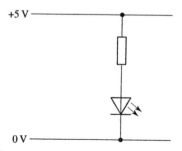

Figure 24.1

  c) Calculate the value of the current limiting resistor needed to make the LED operate under optimum conditions when used with the 5 V power supply.

3 Figure 24.2 shows a potential divider circuit made up from an LDR connected in series with a 2.2 kΩ resistor.

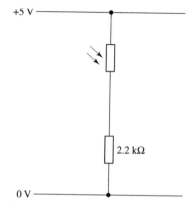

+5 V

2.2 kΩ

0 V

Figure 24.2

  a) Show that when the resistance of the LDR is 30 kΩ the p.d. across the 2.2 kΩ resistor is 0.34 V.

  b) Show that when the resistance of the LDR is 13.5 kΩ the p.d. across the 2.2 kΩ resistor is 0.7 V.

  c) The resistance of the LDR reduces from 13.5 kΩ to 5kΩ. Explain what happens to the p.d. across the 2.2 kΩ resistor.

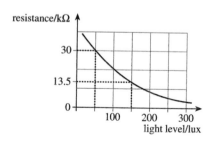

resistance/kΩ

30

13.5

0

100   200   300
light level/lux

Figure 24.3

d) Figure 24.3 shows how the resistance of the LDR varies with light level. The light level reduces from 300 to 50 lux. Describe what happens to the p.d across the 2.2 kΩ resistor.

e) A student constructs a circuit that will switch on a lamp when the light level falls below 150 lux. Figure 24.4 shows her circuit.

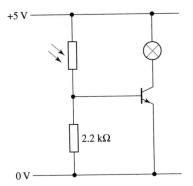

Figure 24.4

The transistor switches when the p.d. between the base and the emitter is 0.7 V.

i) Copy the symbol for the transistor and label the base, collector and emitter connections.

ii) Explain by referring to earlier calculations, why, when the light level is 150 lux, the p.d. across the 2.2 kΩ resistor is 0.7 V.

f) When the student uses the circuit she notices that the lamp lights momentarily. Her teacher suggests that this is due to feedback. Explain the word feedback in the context of this example.

4 Figure 24.5 shows an alternating voltage with a peak voltage of 10 m V. This voltage is used as the input for an amplifier that has a voltage gain of 20.

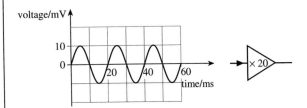

Figure 24.5

a) Copy Figure 24.5 and on the same axes draw a line to show the output voltage.

b) A student wishes to use this output voltage as the input voltage for another amplifier. The second amplifier has a voltage gain of 100 and is powered from a ±15 V power supply. Explain why this amplifier will saturate.

1 A student making revision notes about operational amplifier circuits writes down the following sentences which have some of the words missing. Copy and complete these sentences.

a) *An operational amplifier has two input terminals and one output terminal. The inverting input is labelled the '...' terminal and the ... input is labelled the '+' terminal.*

b) *In amplifier circuits the output of the op-amp is connected back to the input through a resistor. The feedback used in inverting amplifier circuits is ... feedback.*

c) *The negative feedback in op-amp circuits keeps the inverting and non-inverting inputs at the same ....*

d) *The inverting and non-inverting inputs of the operational amplifier have ... input resistance.*

e) *We can identify inverting amplifier circuits as having the following connections:*

  i) *The non-inverting input is joined to the ... line from the power supply.*

  ii) *Part of the output is connected back to the input via a ...*

  iii) *Additionally the input voltage of the amplifier circuit must be connected via a resistor to the ... input of the op-amp.*

2 Figure 25.1 shows a p.d. of 6 V across two resistors in series.

a) Show that the current in each of the resistors is 66 μA.

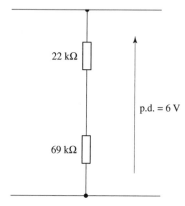

Figure 25.1

b) Show, by calculation, that the p.d. across the 69 kΩ resistor is 4.55 V.

c) Calculate the p.d. across the 22 kΩ resistor.

d) Figure 25.2 shows the potential divider circuit now with the point between the resistors at a potential of 0 V. Copy and complete the diagram to show the voltages, with respect to 0 V, at the points marked X and Y.

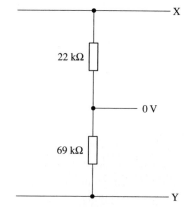

Figure 25.2

e) Figure 25.3 shows a circuit where an op-amp is used to keep the mid point of a potential divider at 0 V.

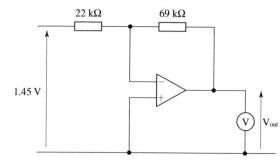

Figure 25.3

  i) What is the current in the 22 kΩ input resistor? Explain your answer.

  ii) Show that the output voltage from the amplifier circuit is −4.55 V.

  iii) Calculate the voltage gain of this amplifier circuit.

  iv) Show, by calculation, that for this circuit

$$V_{out} / V_{in} = -R_f / R_{in}.$$

3 Figure 25.4 shows an inverting amplifier circuit.

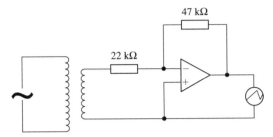

Figure 25.4

a) Calculate the voltage gain of this amplifier circuit.

b) An alternating voltage with a peak value of 1.5 V, as shown in Figure 25.5, is used as the input voltage for this circuit.

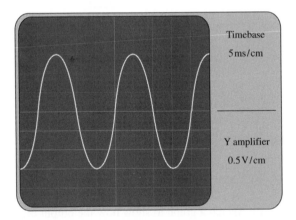

Figure 25.5

i) Calculate the frequency of the input voltage.

ii) Sketch a graph to show BOTH the input and output voltages for this circuit. Your graph should highlight the similarities and differences between the input and output voltages.

c) A student investigating amplifier circuits builds the circuit shown in Figure 25.4. During the testing stage the student notices that the trace on the oscilloscope is as shown in Figure 25.6.

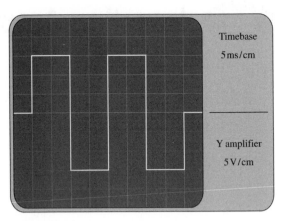

Figure 25.6

She tries to explain this by saying that the square voltage output occurs when the 22 kΩ resistor is short circuited with a piece of wire. Explain why the student is correct in making this statement.

4 A technology student suggests the circuit shown in Figure 25.7 for monitoring light intensity. The resistances of the LDR when in daylight and darkness are as shown in the table.

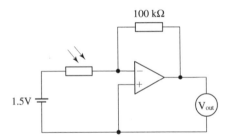

Figure 25.7

	Daylight	Darkness
resistance/kΩ	10	200

a) Show that when the LDR is in darkness the output p.d. of the circuit is -0.75 V.

b) Calculate the output p.d. of the circuit when the LDR is in daylight.

c) Calculate the resistance of the LDR when the output from the circuit is -3.75 V.

26 Inverting Amplifiers 2

1 Figures 26.1 and 26.2 show inverting amplifier circuits constructed using operational amplifiers.

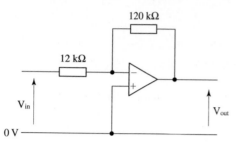

Figure 26.1

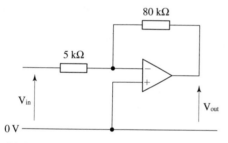

Figure 26.2

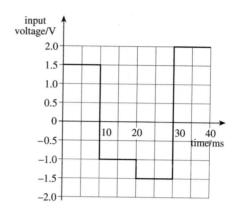

Figure 26.3

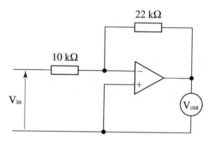

Figure 26.4

a) Show that the gain of the amplifier shown in Figure 26.1 is −10.

b) Calculate the gain of the amplifier shown in Figure 26.2.

c) The p.d. of the output of the circuit in Figure 26.2 is 12 V. Calculate the size of the input p.d.

d) Calculate the input p.d. to the circuit of Figure 26.1 that will result in an output p.d. of 0.75 V.

e) The output of Figure 26.1 is now connected to the input of Figure 26.2.

   i) What input p.d. to the first circuit will result in an output p.d. of 12 V from the second circuit? Explain your answer.

   ii) Show that the overall gain of the two amplifiers is 160.

2 The waveform shown in Figure 26.3 is used as the input to the circuit of Figure 26.4.

a) Calculate the gain of the inverting amplifier circuit shown in Figure 26.4.

b) Calculate the output p.d. from the amplifier when the input is 1.5 V.

c) Sketch a graph to show how the output of the amplifier changes as the input changes as shown in Figure 26.3.

d) The input to the amplifier is altered until the output varies as shown in Figure 26.5. Sketch a graph to show the shape of the input p.d. required to produce this output.

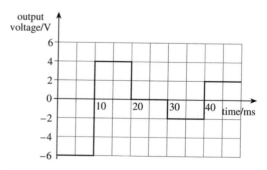

Figure 26.5

3 Figure 26.6 shows a circuit to be investigated by a student studying electronics. The potentiometer allows the input p.d. for the inverting amplifier to be altered between 0 V and −5 V. (The op-amp is powered from a split rail power supply of ±15 V.)

a) Show that when the input p.d. is −1.1 V the output p.d. is 4.45 V.

b) Calculate the input p.d. needed to produce an output p.d. of 15 V.

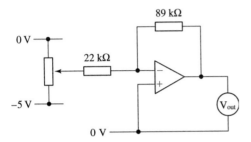

Figure 26.6

input p.d./V	0	−1.1	−2	−3	−4	−5
output p.d./V	0	4.45				

Figure 26.7

c) Calculate the output p.d.s when the inputs are as shown in Figure 26.7.

d) Draw a graph to show how the output p.d. varies as the input p.d. is varied between 0 V and −5 V.

4 A student attempting to understand the advanced amplifier circuit shown in Figure 26.8 simplifies the diagram by considering only the resistors as shown in Figure 26.9.

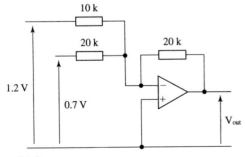

Figure 26.8

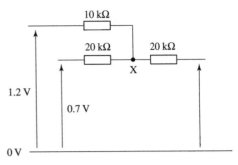

Figure 26.9

The student states that the point marked X in Figure 26.9 is a virtual earth and is at 0 V.

a) Calculate the p.d. across the 20 kΩ input resistor.

b) Show that the current in the 10 kΩ input resistor is 0.12 mA.

c) Show that the current in the 20 kΩ feedback resistor is 0.155 mA.

d) Calculate the p.d. across the 20 kΩ feedback resistor.

e) The function of the op-amp in the circuit of Figure 26.8 is to ensure that point X is maintained at 0 V. What is the output p.d. from the circuit shown in Figure 26.8? Explain your answer.

5 Figure 26.10 shows how the resistance of a thermistor varies with temperature. A student wishes to use this thermistor to make a circuit to monitor temperature. The student's circuit is shown in Figure 26.11.

a) The student places the thermistor in a beaker of water which is at a temperature of 20 °C. Show that the output p.d. from the amplifier circuit is 6 V.

b) The thermistor is now placed in warm water at a temperature of 50 °C. Determine the output p.d. from the amplifier.

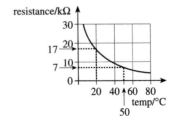

Figure 26.10

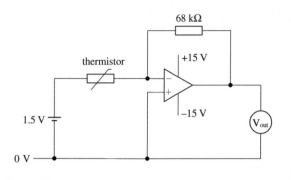

68 kΩ

thermistor

+15 V

−15 V

1.5 V

0 V

V_{out}

Figure 26.11

c) The student notices that when the water is heated above 50 °C the output p.d. from the amplifier remains constant. Explain why this happens and suggest one way in which this fault could be corrected.

27 Difference Amplifiers

1 A student sets up the circuit shown in Figure 27.1.

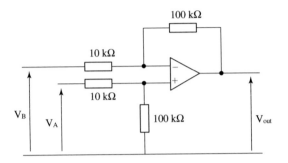

Figure 27.1

a) In what mode is the op-amp operating?

b) State the differential mode gain expression linking the output voltages V_{out} with the input voltages V_A and V_B and the values of the resistances.

c) A student analysing the amplifier draws part of the circuit as shown in Figure 27.2. An input V_A of 1.1 V is connected to the circuit.

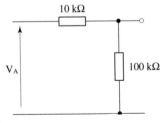

Figure 27.2

   i) Show that the p.d. across the 100 kΩ resistor is 1.0 V.

   ii) Explain why the p.d. at the *inverting* input of the amplifier is 1.0 V.

d) An input V_B of 1.25 V p.d. is connected to the amplifier as shown in Figure 27.1.

   i) Show that the current in the 10 kΩ resistor connected to the inverting input is 25 μA.

   ii) Show that the p.d. across the 100 kΩ resistor is 2.5 V.

   iii) Explain why the output p.d. from the amplifier is −1.5 V.

e) Use your answer to part b) of this question to confirm that the output p.d. from this amplifier circuit is −1.5 V.

2 During her revision of difference amplifier circuits a student considers the Wheatstone Bridge circuit shown in Figure 27.3.

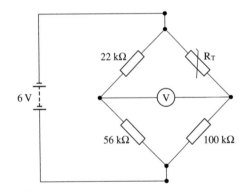

Figure 27.3

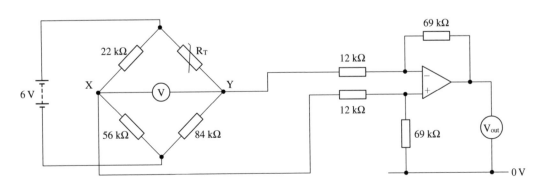

Figure 27.4

a) Show that the p.d. across the 56 kΩ resistor is 4.31 V.

b) Calculate the resistance of the thermistor when the Wheatstone Bridge is balanced.

c) The Wheatstone Bridge is now connected to a difference amplifier as shown in Figure 27.4. The resistance of the thermistor is 36 kΩ.

　　i) Calculate the voltage at Y.

　　ii) Calculate the output p.d. of the amplifier.

d) The resistance of the thermistor varies as shown in Figure 27.5. At what temperature will the output voltage from the amplifier be 0 V? Explain your answer.

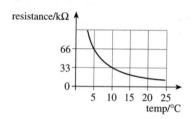

Figure 27.5

3 A student sets up the amplifier as shown in Figure 27.6.

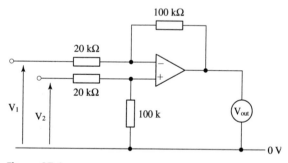

Figure 27.6

The input voltages to the amplifier are provided by signal generators whose output p.d.s vary as shown in Figure 27.7.

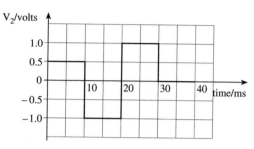

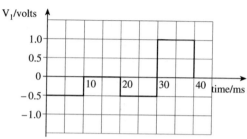

Figure 27.7

Draw a graph to show how the output voltage V_{out} varies during the 40 ms when the input p.d.s are as shown in the graphs of V_1 and V_2.

28 Capacitance, Charge and Potential Difference

1 A student making revision notes on capacitors writes down the following statements:

    I *The capacitance of a system is a measure of how easily the system stores charge.*

    II *The capacitance of a system is numerically the same as the 'charge stored per volt'.*

    III *The quantity of charge stored by a capacitor is directly proportional to the p.d. across the capacitor.*

Which of these statements are correct?
A I and II only
B I and III only
C II and III only
D III only
E I and II and III

2 The current in an LED is 6 mA.
  a) Calculate the quantity of charge passing through the LED in 1 minute.
  b) Calculate the time that it will take for 1 coulomb of charge to pass through the LED.

3 Describe how a student should use the apparatus shown in Figure 28.1 to investigate the relationship between the quantity of charge stored by a capacitor and the p.d. across the capacitor.

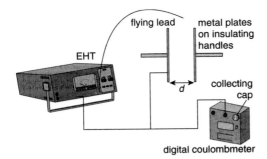

Figure 28.1

  a) Your answer should include:
    i) Details of how you would measure the quantity of charge stored on the capacitor.

    ii) Details of the quantity that you would alter.

    iii) Details of how you would analyse your results to confirm the mathematical relationship between the charge stored and p.d.

  b) The p.d. across a 470 μF capacitor is 900 V. Calculate the quantity of charge stored on the capacitor.

  c) A 470 μF capacitor stores 350 mC of charge. Calculate the p.d. across the capacitor.

4 A photographic flashgun discharges 0.75 C of charge during a flash lasting 20 ms.
  a) Calculate the average current in the flash gun during the flash.
  b) The p.d. across the capacitor in a fully recharged flash gun is 75 V. Calculate the capacitance of the capacitor in the flashgun.

5 Figure 28.2 shows the apparatus being used by a student to investigate the charging of a capacitor.

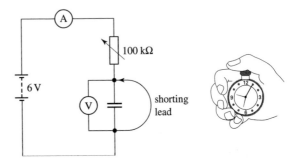

Figure 28.2

  a) Initially with the shorting lead in place the resistance of the variable resistor is set to 100 kΩ. Show that the current in the circuit is 60 μA.
  b) The shorting lead is removed and the capacitor begins to charge. During the charging process the resistance of the variable resistor is reduced so that the current in the circuit remains constant at 60 μA.

     i)   Calculate the p.d. across the resistor
          when the resistance of the variable
          resistor is reduced to 65 kΩ.

     ii) Show that the p.d. across the capacitor is
          2.1 V when the resistance of the variable
          resistor is 65 kΩ.

  c) When the p.d. across the capacitor is 2.1 V
     the charge stored on the capacitor is 10 μC.
     Calculate the capacitance of the capacitor.

  d) Calculate the p.d. across the capacitor when
     the capacitor stores 25.7 μC of charge.

6 Capacitor X in Figure 28.3 has a capacitance of
120 μF and has a p.d. of 9 V across it. When
there is a p.d. of 15 V across capacitor Y it
stores the same quantity of charge as capacitor
X when it has a p.d. of 9 V across it.

Figure 28.3

  a) Calculate the quantity of charged stored by
     capacitor X when it is charged to 9 V.

  b) Calculate the capacitance of capacitor Y.

  c) How much charge will capacitor X store
     when the p.d. across it is 15 V?

29 Charging Capacitors

1 A student investigating the charging of capacitors sets up the circuit shown in Figure 29.1.

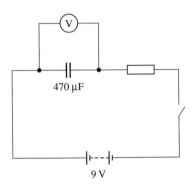

Figure 29.1

a) Sketch a graph to show how the p.d. across the capacitor varies with time after the switch is closed.

b) What is the value of the p.d. across the resistor when the p.d. across the capacitor is 3.2 V? Explain your answer.

c) Add a line to your sketch graph to show how the p.d. across the resistor varies with time as the capacitor charges.

d) Show that the capacitor stores 4.23 mC of charge when fully charged from this battery.

e) At one instant during the charging process the capacitor stores 1.41 mC of charge.
   i) Calculate the p.d. across the capacitor.
   ii) What is the p.d. across the resistor when the capacitor stores 1.41 mC of charge? Explain your answer.

2 The table in Figure 29.2 shows how the charge on the capacitor in the circuit of Figure 29.3 varies with time as the capacitor charges after the switch is closed.

time/s	0	2	5	8	10	12	15
charge/µC	0	208	393	491	529	553	575

Figure 29.2

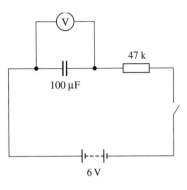

Figure 29.3

a) Plot these results on a graph to show how the charge stored by the capacitor varies with time during the charging process.

b) Use your graph to determine the charge stored by the capacitor 4 seconds after the switch is closed.

c) Show that the p.d. across the capacitor after 5 seconds is 3.93 V.

d) Explain why the p.d. across the resistor after 5 seconds is 2.07 V.

e) Show that the current in the resistor is $44\,\mu A$ when the switch has been closed for 5 seconds.

f) Calculate the current in the resistor 10 seconds after charging begins.

3 The table in Figure 29.4 shows how the p.d. across the capacitor in Figure 29.5 varies with time as the capacitor charges.

time/s	0	10	20	30	40	50
p.d./V	0	3.29	5.37	6.70	7.54	8.07

Figure 29.4

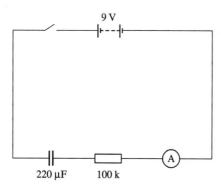

Figure 29.5

time/s	0	10	20	30	40	50
p.d. across resistor/V						
current in resistor/A						

Figure 29.6

a) Plot these results on a graph to show how the p.d. across the capacitor varies with time as the capacitor charges.

b) Estimate the p.d. across the capacitor when it is fully charged. Explain your answer.

c) Calculate the p.d. across the resistor at each of the times shown in the table of Figure 29.4. Enter the values in a copy of the table shown in Figure 29.6.

d) Use the values calculated in c) to determine the current in the resistor at each of the times shown in Figure 29.6.

e) Plot these results on a graph to show how the current in the circuit varies with time during charging.

30 Discharging Capacitors

1 In the circuit shown in Figure 30.1 the 100 µF
   capacitor is initially charged to a p.d. of 12 V.

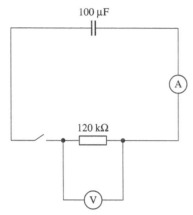

Figure 30.1

a) The switch is now closed. Show that the
   initial value of the current in the circuit is
   100 µA.
b) After a certain time the current in the resistor
   is 35 µA. Calculate the p.d. across the
   resistor at this instant.
c) Calculate the quantity of charge stored by
   the capacitor when the current in the circuit
   is 35 µA.
d) Sketch a graph to show how the p.d. across
   the capacitor varies with time as the
   capacitor discharges. (You need not show
   scales on the graph axes.)
e) The capacitor is again fully charged. The
   120 kΩ resistor is replaced with a 75 kΩ
   resistor. The switch is now closed. Add a
   line to your graph to show how the p.d.
   across the capacitor varies with time as the
   capacitor discharges.

2 A student notices the circuit diagram and
   graph shown in Figure 30.2 in a physics
   textbook in the section on discharging of a
   capacitor. The graph has voltage in volts on the
   y-axis against time in seconds on the x-axis.
   Which one of the following could explain the
   change indicated at the point marked P on the
   graph?

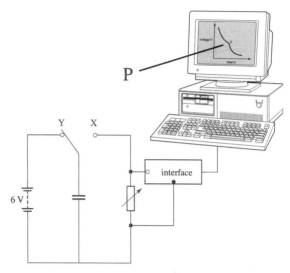

Figure 30.2

A The p.d. of the supply was suddenly
   increased.
B The switch momentarily jumped back from
   X to Y.
C The value of the variable resistor was
   decreased.
D There was a momentary break in the
   connection between the experiment and the
   interface.
E The value of the variable resistor was
   gradually increased.

3 A student sets up the circuit shown in Figure
   30.3 to investigate the discharging of capacitors.
   The student changes the switch from position A
   to position B and records the voltmeter reading
   at 5 second intervals. The results are shown in
   Figure 30.4.

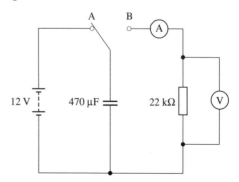

Figure 30.3

time/s	0	5	10	15	20	25
p.d./V	12	7.40	4.56	2.81	1.73	1.07

Figure 30.4

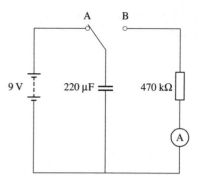

a) Draw a graph to show how the p.d. across the capacitor varies with time as the capacitor discharges.

b) Show that immediately after the switch is moved from A to B the current in the circuit is 0.55 mA.

c) Calculate the current in the resistor at each of the times shown in the table of Figure 30.4. Add these values to a copy of the table shown in Figure 30.5.

time/s	0	5	10	15	20	25
current/mA	0.55					

Figure 30.5

d) Draw a graph to show how the current in the circuit varies with time as the capacitor discharges.

4 The circuit of Figure 30.6 was set up by a student investigating capacitor discharge circuits.

Figure 30.6

a) Calculate the charge stored by the capacitor when the switch is in position A.

b) What is the p.d. across the resistor immediately after the switch is changed to position B? Explain your answer.

c) Calculate the value of the current immediately after the switch is changed to position B.

d) After the capacitor has been discharging for 2 minutes the current in the resistor is 6 μA.

  i) Calculate the p.d. across the resistor at this instant.

  ii) Show that the charge on the capacitor is 620 μC at this instant.

1 A 470 μF capacitor is charged to a p.d. of 9 V. Which of A–E below shows correct values for the charge and energy stored by the capacitor?

	Charge/mC	Energy/mJ
A	52	38
B	4.23	19
C	4.23	38
D	19	86
E	19	38

2 A photographic flashgun discharges 0.5 C of charge in a flash lasting 0.25 s.
  a) Calculate the average current during the discharge.
  b) The capacitor in the flash gun has a p.d. of 125 V across it when fully charged. Calculate the capacitance of the capacitor.
  c) Calculate the energy stored in the fully charged capacitor.
  d) Calculate the average power dissipated in each flash.
  e) An adjustment on the flash gun allows the photographer to set the flash gun so that the flash lasts 0.4 seconds. Explain why the flash of longer duration is not as bright as the shorter one.

3 A student, investigating how the energy stored by a capacitor varies as the p.d. across it is altered, sets up the circuit shown in Figure 31.1.

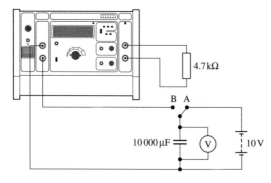

Figure 31.1

a) Show that when the p.d. across the capacitor is 10 V the energy stored in the capacitor is 500 mJ.
b) The table in Figure 31.2 shows how the energy stored by the capacitor varies with charging p.d.

voltage/V	0	2	4	6	8	10	12
energy/mJ	0	20	80	180	320	500	720

Figure 31.2

  i) Draw a graph to show how the energy stored by the capacitor E varies with the p.d. V across the capacitor.
  ii) Use the student's results to determine the relationship between E and V.
  iii) Prove, by calculation, that the student was using a capacitor with a value of 10 000 μF.

4 Capacitor X is charged to a p.d. of 12 V and stores 1.2 mC of charge. When capacitor Y is charged to 10 V it stores the same quantity of energy as X.

Figure 31.3

  a) Calculate the capacitance of capacitor X.
  b) Show that capacitor X stores 7.2 mJ of energy when it is charged to a p.d. of 12 V.
  c) Show that the capacitance of capacitor Y is 144 μF.
  d) The p.d. across each of the capacitors is now halved. Calculate the quantity of energy stored by each of the capacitors.

5 An uncharged 220 μF capacitor is connected in series with a 16 kΩ resistor as shown in Figure 31.4. At one particular instant during the charging process the current in the ammeter is 0.25 mA.
  a) Show that the p.d. across the resistor at this instant is 4 V.
  b) Show that the p.d. across the capacitor at this instant is 2 V.

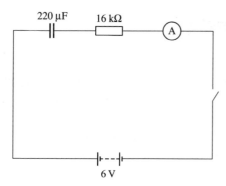

Figure 31.4

c) Calculate the charge stored by the capacitor when the current in the circuit is 0.25 mA.

d) Show that the capacitor stores 0.44 mJ of energy when the current in the circuit is 0.25 mA.

e) Calculate the energy stored by the capacitor when the current in the circuit is 0.12 mA.

6 The 10 000 μF capacitor in Figure 31.5 is initially charged to a p.d. of 20 V. The switch is now closed for 2 minutes and then opened again. At this time the voltmeter indicates that the p.d. across the capacitor has reduced to 12 V.

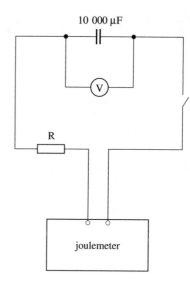

Figure 31.5

a) Calculate the energy stored by the capacitor when it is charged to 20 V.

b) Calculate the energy stored by the capacitor when the p.d. across the capacitor is 12 V.

c) How much energy leaves the capacitor during the 2 minutes that the switch is closed? Explain your answer.

d) Show by calculation that 36% of the initial energy of the capacitor remains when the switch is opened again.

32 Wave Characteristics

1 The clock at a town hall chimes at exactly
   12:00. A student in her classroom hears the
   sound from the chime 1.50 s later. The speed of
   sound in air is 330 ms^{-1}.
   a) Calculate the distance between the classroom
      and the town hall.
   b) The student determines that the sound waves
      from the bell have a frequency of 290 Hz.
      Calculate the periodic time of these waves.
   c) Calculate the wavelength of the sound waves
      from the bell.

2 A student making notes about waves writes
   down the following statements:
   I   Sound waves are longitudinal but light
       waves are transverse.
   II Sound waves, like light waves, transfer
       energy.
   III The quantity of energy transferred
       depends on the amplitude of the wave.

   Which of these statements are correct?
   A I and II and III
   B I and II only
   C II and III only
   D I and III only
   E I only

3 A student making notes on the properties of
   waves writes down the following definitions:
   I   The frequency of a wave is the number
       of waves that pass a given point during
       each second.
   II The wavelength is the distance between
       two identical points on a wave.
   III The wave amplitude is the distance from
       the rest position to the top of a crest or
       the bottom of a trough.

   Which of these statements are correct?
   A I and II and III
   B I and II only
   C II and III only
   D I and III only
   E I only

4 The following passages, describing transverse
   and longitudinal waves are taken from a
   physics textbook. Copy and complete the
   passages.

*In a transverse wave, each part of the medium
through which the wave travels moves at ... to
the direction in which the wave is travelling.*

*As a ... wave moves through a medium the
particles of the medium move to and fro along the
direction in which the energy of the wave travels.*

*... is a longitudinal wave while light and ... are
transverse waves.*

5 An electromagnetic wave has a frequency of
   330 kHz. In which part of the electromagnetic
   spectrum does this wave occur?
   A visible (400–700 nm)
   B radio waves (1 m–1 km)
   C microwaves (1 mm–10 cm)
   D radar (10cm–1 m)
   E ultraviolet (700 nm–1 µm)

6 A sound source produces waves of wavelength
   0.7 m. The sound lasts for 0.5 s and the speed of
   sound through the air is 330 m s^{-1}.
   a) Calculate the frequency of the sound waves.
   b) How many *complete* waves does the sound
      source emit in the 0.5 s?
   c) How far has the front of the first wave
      travelled from the source in 0.5 s?

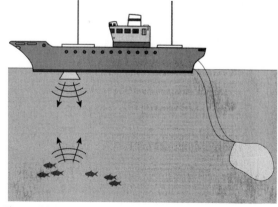

Figure 32.1

7 The sonar system on a ship emits pulses every
   0.45 s. The shape of the emitted pulse and the
   pulse reflected from a shoal of fish are shown in
   Figure 32.2.

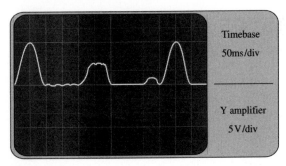

Figure 32.2

Figure 32.3

The timebase of the oscilloscope displaying the shape of the emitted and reflected pulse is set at 50 ms per division.
a) Calculate the time interval between each emitted and reflected pulse.
b) The speed of the sonar pulses through the water is $1500 \, \text{m s}^{-1}$. Calculate the distance between the ship and the shoal of fish.
c) Explain why the shape of the reflected pulse is not as regular as that of the emitted pulse.
d) The ship's captain also notices a very faint reflected pulse 0.37 s after each emitted one. State what you think might be causing this reflected pulse.

8 A newspaper article describing developments in modern technology includes the following statement:
The shape of the satellite-receiving dish concentrates the waves carrying the TV pictures at the receiver.
a) Copy Figure 32.3 and add rays to show how the rays from the satellite are focused by the receiving dish.
The article explains that as amplifiers and receiving circuitry have become more advanced the dishes have become smaller.
b) State the effects of reducing the size of the dish and describe how better amplifiers compensate for smaller sizes of dish.

9 During an earthquake both longitudinal waves and transverse waves are produced. The transverse waves travel straight from the quake to the detecting seismograph with a speed of $8.9 \, \text{km s}^{-1}$. The longitudinal waves travel straight from the quake to the seismograph with a speed of $5.1 \, \text{km s}^{-1}$.
After one particular earthquake the transverse waves are detected 70 s before the longitudinal waves.
Calculate the distance between the earthquake and the detecting seismograph.

33 Snell's Law, Internal Reflection and Critical Angle

1 A student making revision notes about the refraction of light writes down the following statements:

    I   The wavelength of a wave changes when it travels from one medium to a different medium.

    II The ratio sin i/sin r is a constant when light passes obliquely from medium 1 into medium 2.

    III The absolute refractive index of a material depends on the speed of the wave in the medium.

    Which of these statements are correct?

A i and ii and iii
B i and ii only
C ii and iii only
D i and iii only
E ii only

2 A beam of monochromatic light passing from air into a liquid follows the path shown in Figure 33.1.

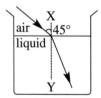

Figure 33.1

  a) Explain, in terms of wavelength, what is meant by 'monochromatic' light .
  b) The refractive index of the liquid for this light is 1.40. Calculate the angle of refraction.
  c) The speed of light in air is $3 \times 10^8\,\mathrm{m\,s^{-1}}$. Show that the speed of light in the liquid is $2.14 \times 10^8\,\mathrm{m\,s^{-1}}$.

3 A beam of monochromatic light of frequency 4.69×10^{14} Hz passes from air into a liquid. The speed of the light in the liquid is $2.05 \times 10^8\,\mathrm{m\,s^{-1}}$.
  a) Calculate the wavelength of the light in air.
  b) Calculate the refractive index of the liquid for this light.
  c) State the frequency of the light in the liquid. Explain your answer.
  d) Calculate the wavelength of the light in the liquid.

4 A ray of monochromatic light from a laser is directed towards the centre of a semicircular block of glass as shown in the diagram. The refractive index of the block is 1.43.

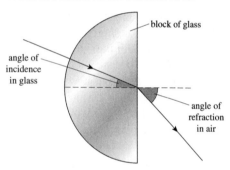

Figure 33.2

    The angles of refraction in air are measured for a number of different angles of incidence in the glass. The results are shown in the following table:

angle of incidence/ degrees	0	5	15	25	35	40
angle of refraction/ degrees	0	7	22	37	55	67

Figure 33.3

  a) Construct a table to include the angles of incidence i, the angles of refraction r and the calculated values of the sine of the angles of incidence and angles of refraction.
  b) Draw a graph of sin i (x-axis) versus sin r (y-axis).

c) Use the gradient of your graph to determine the refractive index of the glass for this light.

d) i) Use your graph to determine the angle of incidence required for the angle of refraction to be 90°.

   ii) What is the value of the critical angle for this light in this material? Explain your answer.

   iii) Use your value for the critical angle to determine a value for the refractive index of the material for this light.

5 A ray of light with a frequency of 5×10^{14} Hz passes from a vacuum into a transparent material which has a refractive index of 1.59.

a) What is the frequency of light in the transparent material? Explain your answer.

b) Calculate the wavelength of the light in the transparent material.

c) Show that the light travels with a speed of 1.89×10^8 m s^{-1} in the material.

6 a) Describe how a student could use the apparatus shown in Figure 33.4 to determine the critical angle for the light in the semicircular glass block. Your answer should include details of how you would assemble the apparatus, which readings you would take and how you would determine the critical angle.

b) Explain how the student could use the value of the critical angle to determine the refractive index of the material for this light.

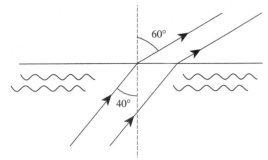

Figure 33.5

7 Figure 33.5 shows a parallel beam of light emerging from an underwater spotlight in an ornamental pond.

a) Show that the refractive index of the water in the pond is 1.35.

b) Calculate the critical angle in the water for this light.

c) When the water in the pond is calm and the pond is viewed from above there appears to be a circular patch of light on the surface of the pond. When there is more water in the pond the circle on the surface of the water is larger. Explain this observation.

8 A ray of monochromatic light is incident at right angles to the surface of a rectangular glass block as shown in Figure 33.6. The centre of the block is a hollow triangular prism which has been filled with water.

The refractive index of the glass relative to air for this light is 1.57.
The refractive index of the water relative to air for this light is 1.43.

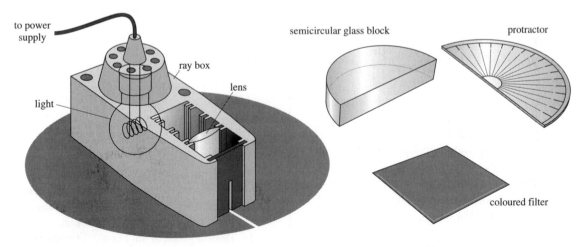

to power supply

ray box

lens

light

semicircular glass block

protractor

coloured filter

Figure 33.4

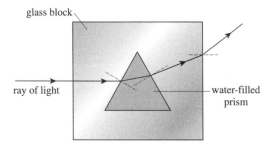

Figure 33.6

a) Explain why the direction of the ray of light does not change as it passes from air into the glass.

b) Calculate the speed of the light in the glass.

c) Calculate the speed of the light in the water.

d) Explain why the light bends away from the normal as it passes from the glass into the water.

9 A student investigating the dispersion of light passes a ray of white light into a glass prism. The angle of incidence for the ray is 60°. The refractive index of the glass prism for red light is 1.517.

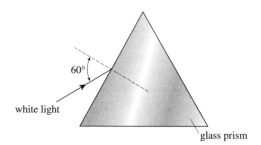

Figure 33.7

The refractive index of the glass prism for blue light is 1.538.

a) Calculate the speed of the red light in the glass prism.

b) Calculate the speed of the blue light in the glass prism.

c) Calculate the angle of refraction in the glass for the red light.

d) Calculate the angle of refraction in the glass for the blue light.

e) The student suggests that using a glass prism with a higher refractive index will cause more dispersion between the red and blue rays leaving the prism. Explain whether or not this is a true statement.

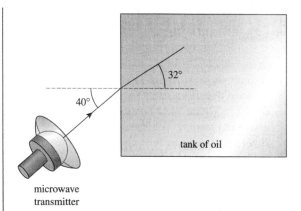

Figure 33.8

10 A narrow beam of microwaves with a wavelength of 3 cm is directed towards a tank of oil as shown in Figure 33.8.

a) Calculate the refractive index of the oil for the microwaves passing from air into the oil.

b) Calculate the critical angle in the oil for the microwaves.

c) A student pours some of this oil into a glass container shaped as shown in Figure 33.9. Copy Figure 33.9 and add a line to show the path of the microwaves through the oil.

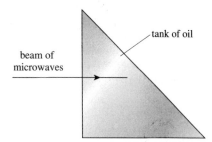

Figure 33.9

d) The student now pours the oil into the glass container shown in Figure 33.10. Copy Figure 33.10 and add a line to show the path of the microwaves through the oil.

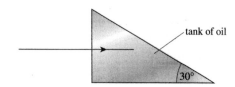

Figure 33.10

34 Interference

1 A microphone is placed at point P, an equal distance from sources of sound X and Y as shown in Figure 34.1. The oscilloscope shows a maximum reading. When a solid object blocks either of the sources the amplitude of the waves shown on the screen reduces.

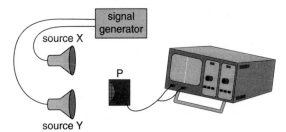

Figure 34.1

The following statements are made:
   I   There is constructive interference at point P.
   II Moving the microphone up or down from P reduces the size of the signal on the oscilloscope.
  III When the microphone is at position P, altering the output frequency from the signal generator changes the amplitude of the signal shown.

Which of these statements are correct?
A I and II and III
B I and II only
C II and III only
D I only
E II only

2 A student describing the word 'coherent' writes down the following statements:
   I   Coherent waves have a constant phase difference throughout their motion.
   II Coherent waves can have different amplitudes.
  III Coherent waves must have the same frequency.

Which of these statements are correct?
A I and II and III
B I and II only
C II and III only
D I only
E II only

3 A student making notes about interference patterns writes the following statements in her notebook:
   I   Maxima of intensity in interference patterns occur at points where waves from two sources arrive in phase.
   II Minima of intensity in interference patterns occur at points where waves from two sources arrive in anti-phase.
  III Interference is evidence for the presence of waves.

Which of these statements are correct?
A I and II and III
B I and II only
C II and III only
D I only
E II only

4 A student investigating the interference of sound waves sets up two loudspeakers, as shown in Figure 34.2, in a room where the walls are designed to minimise sound reflections.

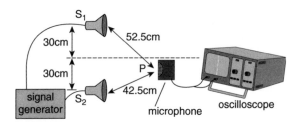

Figure 34.2

The student uses the small microphone attached to the oscilloscope to determine the amplitude of the sound signal detected at different points in the pattern.
a) Explain how the student would recognise when the microphone is at a maximum of intensity in the interference pattern.

The loudspeakers produce sound waves with a frequency of 6400 Hz. A maximum of intensity in the interference pattern is detected at the position shown in Figure 34.2.
b) Calculate the wavelength of the sound waves. The speed of sound in air is $320\,\mathrm{m\,s^{-1}}$.
c) Show that the distance between S_1 and P is

equal to 10½ complete wavelengths of the sound wave.

d) Explain in terms of waves why there is a maximum at P.

5 A student uses the apparatus shown in Figure 34.3 to investigate the interference between an emitted and reflected beam of microwaves.

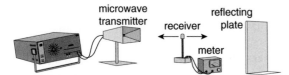

Figure 34.3

a) Explain in terms of waves how interference occurs in this experiment.

b) The probe is placed at a point where the meter indicates a minimum in the intensity pattern. Explain in terms of waves how this minimum is produced.

c) The reflecting plate is moved away from the probe and the reading on the meter increases. Explain, in terms of waves, why the reading increases.

d) The probe is now set at a point where the meter indicates a minimum in the intensity pattern. The reflecting plate is removed. Explain why the reading shown on the meter increases.

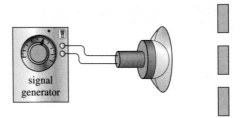

Figure 34.4

6 A student uses the apparatus shown in Figure 34.4 to investigate the interference of sound waves.

a) Explain how the single loudspeaker and plates produce two coherent sources of radiation.

The sound from the loudspeaker has a frequency of 16 000 Hz and the speed of sound in air is 320 m s^{-1}.

b) Calculate the wavelength of the sound waves.

c) Points of maxima and minima in the interference patterns are shown in Figure 34.5.

  i) Point P is 24 cm from source S$_1$. Calculate the distance between P and S$_2$.

  ii) Point Q is 28 cm from source S$_2$. Calculate the distance between Q and S$_1$.

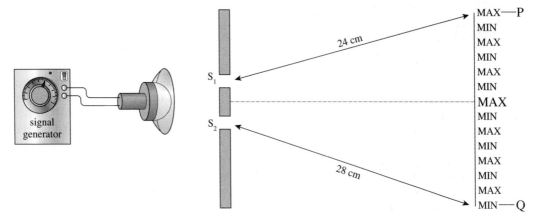

Figure 34.5

35 Diffraction

1 A student makes the following notes about diffraction:

    I Diffraction can be described as the spreading of light into the geometrical shadow.

    II In diffraction experiments on a ripple tank the spreading of waves after they pass through the gap is most obvious when the gap width and the wavelength of the water waves are comparable.

    III In the experiment where light passes through very narrow slits, the pattern produced is as a result of interference between light diffracted at each slit.

Which of these statements are correct?
A I and II and III
B I and II only
C I and III only
D II and III only
E III only

2 Figure 35.1. shows straight waves approaching a barrier in a ripple tank. There are two gaps in the barrier.

Figure 35.1

    a) Copy the diagram and show the shapes of the first three waves after they have passed through the gaps.

    b) After the waves pass through the gaps there is interference between the waves.

      i) On your diagram indicate a point of constructive interference in the interference pattern.

      ii) On your diagram indicate the position of a minimum in the interference pattern.

3 A student making notes about gratings writes down the following points:

    I A grating has an arrangement of closely spaced lines ruled onto a piece of transparent material.

    II Each slit on a grating acts as a source of waves.

    III When laser light is shone onto a grating the interference pattern produced on a screen is a result of both diffraction and interference.

Which of these statements are correct?
A I and II and III
B I and II only
C I and III only
D II and III only
E III only

4 A narrow beam of monochromatic light with a wavelength of 640 nm is directed at a grating which has 500 lines per mm.

    a) What is the colour of the light from this source?

    b) Show, by calculation, that the distance between lines on the grating is 2×10^{-6} m.

    c) At what angle will the second maximum be formed in the interference pattern produced by this grating?

    d) A screen is placed 2 m away from the grating. Calculate the distance between the second maximum on one side of the central maximum and the second maximum on the other side of the central maximum.

    e) This source of light is replaced by a different source which emits monochromatic light of wavelength 589 nm. Explain whether the maxima in the interference pattern will be closer together or further apart than those in the pattern produced with the light of wavelength 640 nm. The screen is still 2 m away from the grating.

36 Irradiance and Photoelectric Effect

1 A student makes the following statements about intensity of radiation:
  I   Irradiance is defined as the power acting on unit area.
  II Irradiance varies inversely with the square of the distance away from the point source.
  III The relationship between irradiance I and distance d can be stated as $I = k/d^2$.

Which of these statements are correct?
  A I and II and III
  B I and II only
  C II and III only
  D I and III only
  E I only

2 A student writes down the following statements about the photoelectric effect:
  I   Photoelectric emission from a metal only occurs when the frequency of the incident radiation is greater than a certain threshold frequency.
  II There are different threshold frequencies of radiation for different metals.
  III When the incident radiation has a frequency below the threshold frequency, an increase in the intensity of the radiation will not cause photoelectric emission.

Which of these statements are correct?
  A I and II and III
  B I and II only
  C II and III only
  D I and III only
  E I only

3 Engineers decide that electricity to power a communications satellite is to be provided by solar cells. The payload of the launching shuttle will only allow for cells with a maximum area of $14\,\text{m}^2$.
At a point 1.5×10^{11} m from the Sun the intensity of the radiation from the Sun is approximately $1500\,\text{W}\,\text{m}^{-2}$.

Figure 36.1

a) Calculate the irradiance at a point 1.45×10^{11} m from the Sun.
b) Show that the maximum energy from the solar cells on the satellite is $22\,470$ W when the satellite is 1.45×10^{11} m from the Sun.
c) The efficiency of the solar cells is quoted as 16%. Calculate the maximum electrical power produced by $14\,\text{m}^2$ of solar cells.
d) The engineers decide that since the satellite requires a constant power of $3.6\,\text{k}\Omega$ of electricity they will not be able to use solar cells. Explain how they arrived at this answer.

4 A student investigating the photoelectric effect shines light from different sources of radiation onto a clean piece of zinc placed on top of the charge measuring device shown in Figure 36.2.

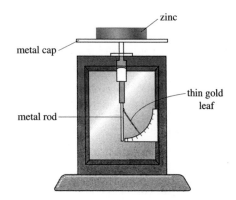

metal cap
zinc
thin gold leaf
metal rod

Figure 36.2

a) Explain the meanings of the terms *work function* and *threshold frequency*.

b) Explain the following observations in terms of the work function and threshold frequency:

   i) The negatively charged leaf falls slowly when light from a mercury lamp shines on the zinc.

   ii) The positively charged leaf does not rise when light from a mercury lamp shines on the zinc.

   iii) The negatively charged leaf does not fall when light from a source of red light shines on the zinc.

   iv) Increasing the intensity of the red light has no effect on the leaf when the leaf is negatively charged.

5 In the apparatus shown in Figure 36.3 ultraviolet light with a wavelength of 254 nm shines on a zinc plate.

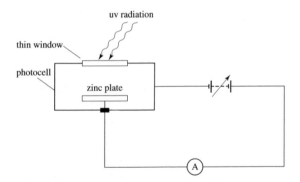

uv radiation

thin window

photocell

zinc plate

A

Figure 36.3

a) Calculate the energy of a photon of light with this wavelength.

b) A student analysing the situation makes the statement that each photon of uv radiation releases a photoelectron from the zinc. What conclusion can be made about the work function of zinc? Explain your answer.

c) The current in the circuit is $4\,\mu A$. How many photoelectrons are released per second from the zinc?

d) The zinc surface has an area of $9\,cm^2$. Calculate the total energy arriving on the zinc surface during each second.

e) Calculate the irradiance of the uv radiation at the surface of the zinc.

6 A lamp emits monochromatic light with a wavelength of 254 nm. The intensity of this light falling on a clean zinc surface is $0.5\,W\,m^{-2}$.

a) Calculate the energy of one photon of this radiation.

b) The threshold frequency of radiation for zinc corresponds to a wavelength of 310 nm. Calculate the value of the work function of zinc.

c) Calculate the maximum kinetic energy of an electron emitted from the zinc.

d) Calculate the number of photons of radiation per m^2 arriving at the zinc during one second.

37 Emission and Absorption Spectra

1 A student writes down the following statements about spectra:

   I *The atoms in a low pressure gas in a discharge tube are thought of as being 'free' atoms.*

   II *The electrons in a free atom occupy discrete energy levels.*

   III *The power supply connected across the discharge tube provides the energy to excite the atoms in the gas.*

Which of these statements are correct?
A I and II and III
B I and II only
C II and III only
D I and III only
E III only

2 The diagram below shows three of the possible energy levels within a hydrogen atom.

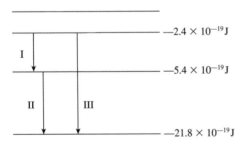

Figure 37.1

a) What is meant by describing an atom as being in an 'excited' state?

b) Calculate the energy released when an electron makes the transition labelled I in Figure 37.1.

c) Calculate the frequency of a photon released when an electron makes the transition labelled II in Figure 37.1.

d) Which transition, I, II or III results in the release of radiation with the longest wavelength? Explain your answer.

3 White light is shone through a sample of gas at low pressure in a tube, as in Figure 37.2. The spectrum of the emerging light is observed using a grating.
This spectrum, when examined closely, looks very similar to the spectrum of the light from

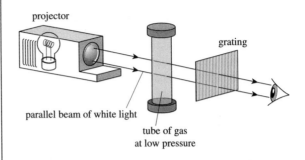

Figure 37.2

the source alone. However, occasional black lines are observed in the spectrum of the light which has passed through the tube.

a) Explain the purpose of the grating in observing the white light spectrum.

b) Explain why light with certain frequencies is missing from the spectrum of light which has passed through the gas.

c) Explain how the black lines in an absorption spectrum can give an indication of the type of gas through which the white light passes.

4 A student making notes about absorption spectra writes down the following statements:

   I An absorption line occurs in a spectrum when an electron in energy level W_1 absorbs a photon of radiation of frequency f and is excited to energy level W_2 where $W_2 = W_1 + hf$.

   II The energies of electron transitions which cause the black lines in the absorption spectrum for a gas are the same as the energies of electron transitions producing the emission spectrum for the gas.

   III Black lines in the spectrum of sunlight can be described as absorption lines.

Which of these statements are correct?
A I and II and III
B I and II only
C II and III only
D II only
E III only

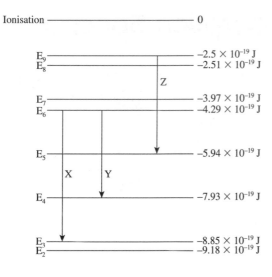

Ionisation —————————————— 0

E_9 ———————— -2.5×10^{-19} J
E_8 ———————— -2.51×10^{-19} J

Z

E_7 ———————— -3.97×10^{-19} J
E_6 ———————— -4.29×10^{-19} J

E_5 ———————— -5.94×10^{-19} J

X   Y

E_4 ———————— -7.93×10^{-19} J

E_3 ———————— -8.85×10^{-19} J
E_2 ———————— -9.18×10^{-19} J

E_1 ———————— -16.61×10^{-19} J

Figure 37.3

5 Figure 37.3 shows the energy level diagram for a mercury atom.
  a) In one excited mercury atom the electron is in the energy state labelled E_5. Calculate the energy that will be required to raise this electron into energy level E_8.
  b) Calculate the wavelength of the photons that will be absorbed when the electron moves from level E_5 to E_8.
  c) Calculate the wavelengths of the radiation that you would expect to find in the mercury emission caused by the transitions labelled X, Y and Z in Figure 37.3
  d) The four brightest lines in the emission spectrum of mercury have wavelengths of 405 nm, 436 nm, 546 nm and 578 nm. Copy Figure 37.3 and identify the electron transitions responsible for the emission of radiation of these wavelengths.

6 The laser used in one brand of CD players emits monochromatic light of wavelength 840 nm.
  a) When this light passes through a grating only one bright line is seen in the emission spectrum. Explain why only one line appears in the emission spectrum of the laser.
  b) Calculate the difference in energy between the two energy levels that produce photons with this wavelength.

38 Lasers and Semiconductors

1 A student makes the following statements about semiconductors:

   I   Spontaneous emission of radiation is a random process analogous to the radioactive decay of a nucleus.

   II   When radiation of energy hf is incident on an excited atom the atom may be stimulated to emit a photon of energy hf.

   III   In stimulated emission the incident and emitted radiations are in phase and travel in the same direction.

Which of these statements are correct?

A   I and II and III
B   I and II
C   I and III
D   II only
E   III only

2 A student makes the following statements about semiconductors:

   I   Doping is a process where the resistance of an insulator is reduced by adding small quantities of impurity atoms.

   II   In an n-type semiconductor the majority of charge carriers are negatively charged.

   III   Increasing the quantity of doping atoms reduces the resistance of a semiconductor.

Which of these statements are correct?

A   I and II and III
B   I and II
C   I and III
D   II only
E   III only

3 When the light from a light emitting diode (LED) is examined with a spectroscope it is found to be monochromatic.

  a) Explain the meaning of the word *monochromatic*.

  b) Explain why this LED is not emitting laser light.

4 Figure 38.1 shows the number of electrons in the outer shells of atoms of certain elements.

  a) Draw a diagram to show how the electrons in a sample of pure silicon bond the atoms together.

Element	Symbol	Atomic no.	No of electrons
Arsenic	As	33	5
Silicon	Si	14	4
Indium	In	49	3

Figure 38.1

  b) Explain the meaning of the term *covalent bond*.

  c) What type of semiconductor will be formed when pure silicon is doped with small quantities of arsenic? Explain your answer.

  d) What are the majority charge carriers in a sample of silicon doped with arsenic? Explain your answer.

  e) Does doping a sample of pure silicon with arsenic produce material with an overall negative charge? Explain your answer.

5 Figure 38.2 shows a diagram which appears in many textbooks to explain the operation of a laser.

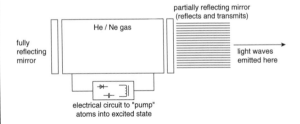

Figure 38.2

  a) Explain the functions of the totally and partially reflecting mirrors.

  b) The wavelength of the light emitted by an argon ion laser is 488 nm. The output power from the laser is 2 W.

    i) Calculate the energy of a photon of the emitted radiation.

    ii) Calculate the number of photons emitted by the laser during each second.

iii) The partially reflecting mirror only permits 1% of the radiation in the tube to be released. Estimate the number of photons within the laser.

c) The beam of light emitted by this laser has a diameter of 1.5 mm.
  i) Show that the beam produced by the laser has a cross-sectional area of $1.77 \times 10^{-6}\,\text{m}^2$.
  ii) Calculate the irradiance of the radiation released by the laser.

6 A textbook states that when a small quantity of arsenic atoms are added to a sample of pure silicon an n-type semiconductor is formed.

a) Is pure silicon a conductor, an insulator or a semiconductor? Explain your answer.

b) Explain how doping a pure semiconductor with arsenic atoms can form an n-type semiconductor.

c) What are the majority charge carriers when silicon is doped with arsenic?

d) A sample of pure silicon is doped with indium atoms. Explain how doping the pure silicon with indium atoms produces a p-type semiconductor.

e) Another sample of pure silicon is doped with indium atoms. What are the majority charge carriers in the material produced? Explain your answer.

39 p–n Junctions and Photodiodes

1 A student making notes about photodiodes writes the following statements :

   I A photodiode is a solid state device in which positive and negative charges are produced by the action of light on a p–n junction.

   II A photodiode used in the photovoltaic mode can supply power to a load.

   III A photodiode used in the photoconductive mode may be used as a light sensor.

Which of these statements are correct?

A I and II and III
B I and II only
C I and III only
D II and III only
E I only

2 A textbook states that:

When p-type and n-type materials come together some of the electrons in the n-type diffuse across into holes in the p-type while some holes from the p-type diffuse into the n-type to be filled by electrons. As a consequence of this a depletion layer is formed.

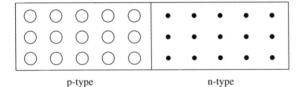

p-type   n-type

Figure 39.1

  a) Figure 39.1 represents a situation where n-type and p-type materials are brought in contact. Copy this diagram and indicate how the charge carriers diffuse to form a depletion layer.

  b) Explain how a p.d. is set up across the depletion layer.

  c) Indicate on your copy of Figure 39.1 which side of the depletion layer is positive and which side is negative.

  d) Explain how connecting the positive of a battery to the n-type material and the negative of the battery to the p-type material widens the depletion layer.

3 a) Draw a diagram to show a 0–6 V power supply connected to a resistor, an ammeter and a forward biased diode. Clearly indicate the polarity of the terminals of the power supply.

  b) Figure 39.2 shows the current–voltage characteristic of the diode connected to the power supply. Explain why the output p.d. from the power supply must be raised above 0.7 V before the ammeter registers a current.

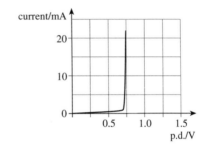

Figure 39.2

  c) The p.d. across the diode stays at a constant 0.7 V while the output p.d. from the power supply rises from 1 V to 6 V. Show that the p.d. across the resistor connected in series with this forward biased diode is 5.3 V when the p.d. of the supply is 6 V.

4 A diode is connected is series with a resistor and an alternating voltage supply as shown in Figure 39.3.

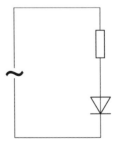

Figure 39.3

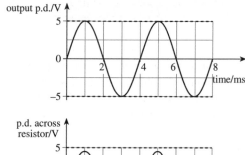

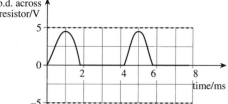

Figure 39.4

a) The output voltage from the supply and the
p.d. across the resistor are shown in
Figure 39.4.
   i)   Calculate the frequency of the output
        voltage of the supply.
   ii) The peak voltage of the output from the
        supply is 5 V. The peak p.d. across the
        resistor is 4.3 V. Explain why this
        difference in values occurs.

5 A textbook describing light emitting diodes
   (LEDs) states that:

   *When there is a current in a forward biased
   diode some of the electrons in the n-type side
   recombine with holes from the p-type. The result
   is a more stable arrangement that can produce
   photons of light.*

   a) Explain what is meant by a *forward biased
      diode*.
   b) The light from an LED is observed with a
      grating that is labelled as having 300 lines
      per mm. The first bright line in the emission
      spectrum of the radiation from the LED is
      observed at an angle of 8.8° from the centre.
      i)   Calculate the wavelength of the
           radiation emitted by the LED.
      ii) What colour of light is emitted by the
           LED? Explain your answer.
      iii) Calculate the energy of a photon
           produced when an electron and hole
           recombine in this LED.

6 A student writes the following statement about
   photodiodes:

   *When a normal diode is connected in reverse
   bias to a power supply there is usually no
   current in the diode. When a photodiode is
   connected in reverse bias and light falls on the
   p–n junction a small current called the leakage
   current is produced.*

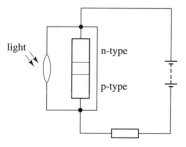

Figure 39.5

   a) Explain why increasing the intensity of the
      light causes more current in the reverse
      biased photodiode.
   b) Figure 39.6 shows a technology student's
      design for a 'fast response light switch'.

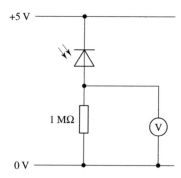

Figure 39.6

      i)   When light shines on the photodiode the
           reading on the voltmeter is almost 5 V.
           Explain why the reading is high.
      ii) Explain why the reading on the
           voltmeter fall to almost 0 V when no
           light shines on the photodiode.
      iii) State one reason why the student prefers
           to use a photodiode rather than an LDR
           for this 'fast response light switch'.

7 Figure 39.7 shows a photodiode connected to a
   very high resistance digital voltmeter.
   a) Explain how photons of light shining

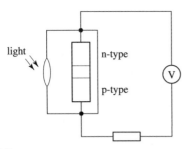

Figure 39.7

through the window of the photodiode onto the p–n junction can produce a p.d. across the ends of the photodiode.

b) In which mode is the photodiode operating when connected as shown in Figure 39.7?

c) Explain why solar panels made from photodiodes are more widely used on satellites in space than they are in ground based applications.

40 Nuclear Changes

1 A student writes down the following statements about Rutherford's famous alpha particle scattering experiment:

   I The fact that most of the alpha particles passed through the thin gold foil without deviation means that most of the volume inside the atom is empty space.

   II The alpha particles were deflected by positively charged centres of charge. The closer an alpha particle came to one of these centres the further it was deviated from its straight through position.

   III The rebounding of a few of the alpha particles was caused by very small regions where the mass of the atom was concentrated. These regions are called nuclei.

Which of these statements are correct?

A I and II and III
B I and II only
C II and III only
D I and II only
E III only

2 The element uranium has an atomic number of 92 and is represented in equations by the symbol U. Three isotopes of uranium have mass numbers of 234, 235 and 238.

  a) How many protons are there in each atom of uranium? Explain your answer.

  b) Explain what is meant by the mass number of an element.

  c) Explain the meaning of the word isotope.

  d) Write the symbols that represent the three different isotopes of uranium.

  e) Calculate the number of neutrons in each of these three isotopes of uranium.

3 The uranium-238 isotope decays by alpha emission.

  a) Explain what is meant by an alpha particle.

  b) The atomic number of uranium is 92. Write an equation series to show how a uranium atom decays to produce a thorium (Th) atom by alpha emission.

  c) Calculate the number of neutrons in an atom of thorium. Show all your reasoning.

4 The radioactive isotope lead-209 decays into bismuth-209 by emitting a beta particle.

$$^{208}_{82}\text{Pb} \rightarrow {}^{208}\text{Bi} + \beta$$

  a) Copy and complete the decay equation to show this beta decay.

  b) Explain the changes that take place in the nucleus of the lead atom during a beta decay.

  c) Explain how the beta particle emitted during the decay differs from an electron in the region surrounding the nucleus of the lead atom.

5 The radioactive isotope uranium-234 decays into thorium by the emission of an alpha particle. The thorium atoms formed then also decay by alpha emission into radium. This decay is represented by the partially completed equation.

$$^{234}_{92}\text{U} \rightarrow {}_{90}\text{Th} \rightarrow {}^{226}\text{Ra}$$

  a) Copy the equation and add the missing mass and atomic number values.

  b) Show, by calculation, that each nucleus of uranium-234 contains 92 protons and 142 neutrons.

  c) Calculate the number of protons and neutrons in each of the elements involved in this decay series.

  d) Decay series can be summarised in the type of diagram shown in Figure 40.1. Copy Figure 40.1 and add points to show the positions of the thorium and radium atoms.

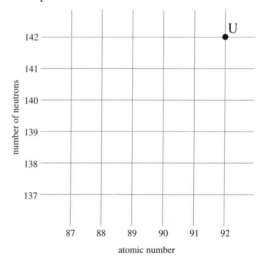

Figure 40.1

6 In Rutherford's famous experiment alpha particles were fired at gold foil. In another Rutherford experiment, alpha particles were fired at a sample of nitrogen atoms.

$$\,^{4}_{2}\text{He} + \,^{14}_{7}\text{N} \rightarrow \,^{17}_{8}\text{O} + \text{X}$$

a) Find the number of protons and neutrons in the particle X produced as a result of the interaction between the alpha particles and the nitrogen atoms.

b) In another experiment beryllium atoms were bombarded with alpha particles.

$$\,^{4}_{2}\text{He} + \,^{9}_{4}\text{Be} \rightarrow \,^{12}_{6}\text{C} + \text{Y}$$

Calculate the number of protons and neutrons in particle Y produced as a result of the interaction between the alpha particles and the beryllium atoms.

7 In 1934 Marie Curie's daughter, Irene Joliot-Curie, and her husband, Frederic Joliot, bombarded aluminium atoms with alpha particles.

$$\,^{4}_{2}\text{He} + \,^{27}_{13}\text{Al} \rightarrow \,^{x}_{y}\text{Q} + \,^{1}_{0}\text{n}$$

a) Calculate the atomic and mass numbers for the element Q formed as a result of this interaction.

b) Use the information given in the table of Figure 40.2 to determine the identity of element Q.

name	isotope symbol	number of protons	number of neutrons
Sodium	$\,^{23}_{11}\text{Na}$	11	12
Phosphorus	$\,^{30}_{15}\text{P}$	15	15
Silicon	$\,^{28}_{14}\text{Si}$	14	14

Figure 40.2

41 Fission and Fusion

1 A student writes down the following statements about fission and fusion:

   I   In fission, a nucleus with a large mass number splits into two nuclei of smaller mass number, and usually there are some neutrons produced as a result.

   II   In some radioisotopes, fission is spontaneous while in others it is induced.

   III   In fusion, two nuclei with small mass numbers combine to form a single nuclide with a larger mass number.

   Which of these statements are correct?
   A I and II and III
   B I and III only
   C II and III only
   D I and II only
   E III only

2 A textbook states that:
   The total kinetic energy of the products of a nuclear fission exceeds that of the bombarding neutron and the target atom.
   a) Explain the source of this kinetic energy. Include in your answer the words *mass loss* and refer to an appropriate equation.
   b) In one particular nuclear fission the mass loss for each fission is 3.57×10^{-28} kg. Show that the energy produced for each fission is 3.21×10^{-11} J. (Speed of light $= 3 \times 10^8$ m s^{-1}.)
   c) Show that 2.025×10^{19} fissions per second will produce a total output power of 650 MW.

3 A nuclide of uranium-235 undergoes fission when it is bombarded with neutrons. The reaction can be summarised in the following equation:

$$^{235}_{92}U + {}^1_0n \rightarrow {}^{92}_{36}Kr + {}^{141}_{56}Ba + 3\,{}^1_0n$$

   a) Use the data in Figure 41.1 to show that the mass loss for each fission is 3.2×10^{-28} kg.
   b) Show, by calculation, that the energy released per fission is 2.88×10^{-11} J.
   c) There are approximately 2.56×10^{24} atoms in each 1 kg of uranium-235. Estimate the theoretical quantity of energy that could be released by the fission of 1 kg of uranium-235.

Element	Mass/kg
$^{235}_{92}U$	3.9014×10^{-25}
$^{92}_{36}Kr$	1.5255×10^{-25}
$^{141}_{56}Ba$	2.3392×10^{-25}
^1_0n	1.6750×10^{-27}

Figure 41.1

4 **a)** Explain the meaning of the term *chain reaction*.
   b) One particular type of nuclear reactor uses boron control rods. Describe the purpose of the control rods in this type of reactor.
   c) One type of nuclear reactor uses graphite blocks as the moderator. Describe the purpose of the moderator in the reactor.
   d) Describe the purpose of the coolant in a nuclear reactor.
   e) Describe the purpose of the containment vessel. State two properties that a material must have to be suitable for use as a containment vessel.

5 State the type of nuclear reaction represented by the following equation

$$^2_1H + {}^2_1H \rightarrow {}^3_2e + {}^1_0n$$

   a) Use the data in Figure 41.2 to show that the mass loss for each fission is 1.0×10^{-29} kg.

Element	Atomic mass/kg
^2_1H	3.345×10^{-27}
^3_2He	5.005×10^{-27}
^1_0n	1.675×10^{-27}

Figure 41.2

   b) Show, by calculation, that the energy released by one of these reactions is 9×10^{-13} J.
   c) Explain why very high temperatures are required to make the reaction shown in this equation happen.

42 Radiation and Matter

1 A student writes down the following statements about the ionising effects of radiation:

   I   Alpha particles produce much greater ionisation density than beta particles or gamma rays.

   II Ionising radiations can kill or change the nature of living cells.

   III Ionising radiation is easy to detect and can be used as a tracer in medical applications.

Which of these statements are correct?

A I and II and III
B I and III only
C II and III only
D I and III only
E II only

2 A student makes notes on the harm that ionising radiation can do to living cells. He states that biological harm depends on:

   I   The energy of the absorbed particles.

   II The type of radiation and the type of tissue irradiated.

   III The mass of the matter which is absorbing the radiation and the duration of the exposure to radiation .

Which of these statements are correct?

A I and II and III
B I and III only
C II and III only
D I and III only
E II only

3 The radiation weighting factors for different types of radiation are as shown in Figure 42.1.

  a) Explain why it is necessary to assign a weighting factor to the different types of radiation.

Type of radiation	W_R
α	20
β	1
γ and X rays	1
slow neutrons	2.3
fast neutrons	10

Figure 42.1

  b) Explain why alpha particles have a larger W_R value than X-rays or gamma rays.

  c) A sample of tissue of mass 2 kg is irradiated with a total of 25 J of gamma radiation.

    i)   Calculate the absorbed dose of radiation.

    ii) Show that the equivalent dose of this radiation is numerically the same as the absorbed dose.

    iii) Explain why the dose equivalent and the absorbed dose are numerically the same.

    iv) For which types of radiation shown in Figure 42.1 will the absorbed dose and the equivalent dose be numerically the same?

4 The table shown in Figure 42.2 lists typical absorbed doses associated with common diagnostic techniques.

Examination	Typical absorbed dose
chest X-ray	0.27 mGy
barium meal	17 mGy
dental X-ray	0.1 mGy
leg X-ray	0.12 mGy

Figure 42.2

  a) During a course of treatment a man with a chest mass of 16 kg has four chest X-rays. Calculate the energy of the radiation received by the chest tissue during the course of treatment.

  b) Explain why the radiographer administering the treatments takes special care to protect himself while the patient is receiving the radiation treatment.

5 A sample of tissue with a mass of 15 g is irradiated using a source that emits alpha, beta and gamma radiations. During the exposure the absorbed equivalent dose from the alpha radiation is 40 mSv. (The quality factors are shown in Figure 42.1.)

  a) Show that the sample absorbs 30 µJ of energy from the alpha source.

  b) The sample also absorbs 20 µJ from the beta source and 15 µJ of energy from the gamma source. Calculate the total equivalent dose for all the radiations.

6 A sample of tissue of mass 20 g is placed close to two sources. One source emits alpha radiation while the other is a beta emitter. The activities of the sources are as shown in Figure 42.3

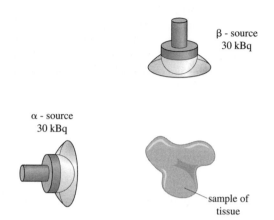

β - source
30 kBq

α - source
30 kBq

sample of
tissue

Figure 42.3

a) What is the number of disintegrations from the alpha source per second? Explain your answer.

In analysing the maximum potential for harm from this situation a health physicist assumes that all of the disintegrations from both sources produce particles which irradiate the sample of tissue.

b) The absorbed equivalent dose rate for radiation from the alpha source is $0.15\,\mu$ Sv s^{-1}. Show that the energy of each alpha particle is 7.5×10^{-15} J. (The quality factors are shown in Figure 42.1.)

c) The beta particles have an average energy of 2×10^{-13} J. Calculate the equivalent dose rate for radiation from the beta source.

d) Calculate the total energy absorbed by the sample in 1 hour.

43 Half-Life and Half Value Thickness

1 Figure 43.1 shows how a radioactive source can be used to monitor the thickness of paper in a rolling mill.

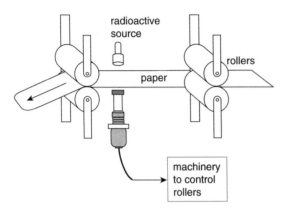

Figure 43.1

a) Explain how the radioactive source can be used to indicate when the paper is thinner than required.

b) An engineer suggests that the process should use a gamma source to monitor the thickness of the paper. Explain why this choice is unsuitable.

c) Should this process use a radioisotope with a long or with a short half-life? Explain your answer.

2 A radioactive source has an initial activity of 12 MBq and a half-life of 35 s.

a) Show that the activity of the source after 3.5 minutes is 187.5 kBq.

b) What fraction of the initial material remains after 105 s? Explain your answer.

c) Calculate the time taken for the activity of the sample to fall to 0.75 MBq.

3 a) Lead-212 decays by emitting a beta particle. Copy and complete the following equation to show the atomic and mass numbers of the daughter nuclide.

$$^{212}_{82}\text{Pb} \rightarrow \text{Bi} + \beta$$

b) The sample of lead-212 is monitored at regular intervals using the apparatus shown in Figure 43.2. The count rates are recorded in the table shown in Figure 43.3.

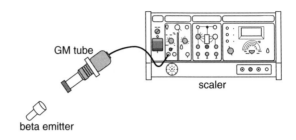

Figure 43.2

time/h	0	5	10	15	20	25	30	35	40	45
counts min^{-1}	156	119	94	76	63	54	47	42	39	36

Figure 43.3

i) A few days after the experiment has started the count rate remains at a constant value of 30 counts per minute. Explain the origin of the radiation causing this count rate.

ii) Calculate the corrected count rate for each of the times in the table.

iii) Draw a graph of corrected count rate versus time for the decay of this radioisotope of lead.

iv) From your graph determine an average value for the half-life of this sample of lead-212.

4 A student making revision notes about radiation protection writes down the following statements:

  I The background radiation in the environment comes from both natural and artificial sources.

  II A gamma source of radiation behaves as a point source so the intensity of gamma radiation decreases as $1/d^2$.

  III The average effective equivalent dose that a person in the UK receives due to natural sources is approximately 2 mSv.

Which of these statements are correct?

A I and II and III
B I and II only
C II and III only
D II only
E III only

5 A health physicist designs a container for storing a radioactive gamma source. The suggested design is as shown in Figure 43.4.

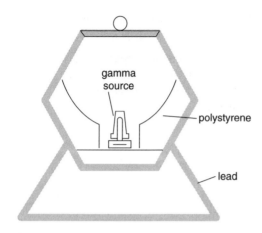

Figure 43.4

The light polystyrene packaging inside the container is designed to hold the source in the centre of the castle. The walls of the castle are made from lead shielding with a thickness of 24 mm.

a) A Geiger-Muller (GM) tube is placed against the outside of the container and registers a count rate of 20 counts per minute above background levels. Calculate the maximum count rate that would be expected if the source is removed from the container and kept at the same distance from the GM tube. (The half-value thickness of this type of lead is 8 mm).

b) The health physicist finds that it is acceptable to have a count rate of 25 counts per minute, above background, outside the lead container. Use a graphical technique to find the minimum thickness of lead that would reduce the count rate outside the lead container to 25 counts per minute above background levels.

Multiple Choice and Matching Questions

MC1: Distance, Displacement and Speed

1 The average speed of a moving object can be calculated by the arithematical law:

A Average speed = $\dfrac{\text{distance travelled}}{\text{total journey time}}$

B Average speed = $\dfrac{\text{distance}}{\text{travelled}} \times \dfrac{\text{total journey}}{\text{time}}$

C Average speed = $\dfrac{\text{total journey time}}{\text{total distance travelled}}$

D Average speed = $\dfrac{\text{total distance travelled}}{0.5 \times \text{total journey time}}$

E Average speed = total journey time × total distance travelled

2 In the qualifying lap for a motor racing Grand Prix, one driver completes the 1.8 km circuit in 40 seconds. Her average speed for the lap is:
A 0.045 m s^{-1}
B 22 m s^{-1}
C 40 m s^{-1}
D 45 m s^{-1}
E 72 m s^{-1}

3 A modern high-speed train completes a 1 hour 15 minutes journey at an average speed of 72 km h^{-1}. The distance travelled by the train during this journey is:
A 63 km
B 80 km
C 83 km
D 90 km
E 108 km

4 Which ONE of the following statements about distance and displacement is FALSE?
A Distance and displacement are both measured in metres.
B Displacements must indicate a direction.
C Distances and displacements never have the same size.
D Displacements indicate both the magnitude and the direction that an object is away from the reference point.

E Objects can travel different distances to achieve the same displacement.

5 Figure 44.1 shows the apparatus that a student is using to measure the instantaneous speed of a trolley at certain points as it travels down an inclined runway.

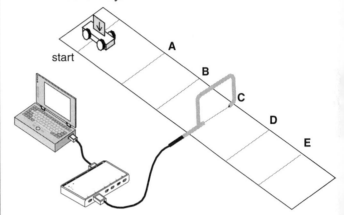

Figure 44.1

She is trying to work out the speed at the point marked A on the runway. Which of the following measurements does she have to make where I = the time that the light gate is interrupted, II = the length of the interrupt card and III = the mass of the trolley:
A I only
B I and II only
C I and III only
D II and III only
E I, II and III

6 In an orienteering event a runner runs 8 km in a North Easterly direction (045) and then 4 km due south. At the end of the race her displacement from the starting point is:
A 12.0 km north east of the start
B 5.9 km on a bearing of 074
C 4.0 km on a bearing of 045
D 12.0 km on a bearing of 180
E 11.2 km on a bearing of 063

7 At the end of a motor car rally the leader has covered 84.75 km of special stages in a time of 45 minutes. The average speed of the driver over the special stages is:

A $1.88\,\text{km h}^{-1}$
B $1.94\,\text{km h}^{-1}$
C $113\,\text{km h}^{-1}$
D $194\,\text{km h}^{-1}$
E $188\,\text{km h}^{-1}$

8 A student studying mechanics notes that the displacement versus time graph shown in Figure 44.2 has both positive and negative sections.

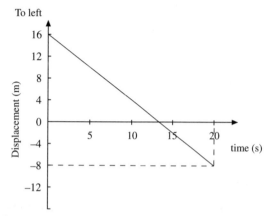

Figure 44.2

The student makes the following statements about the graph:

I The object begins it motion 16 m to the left of the observation point.

II After 10 seconds the object is 4 m to the left of the observation point.

III During the 20 seconds of the motion the object travels a total distance of 24 m.

Which of these statements is/are correct

A II only
B I and II only
C I and III only
D I and III only
E I and II and III

MC2: Velocity and Acceleration

1 The average velocity of a moving object can be calculated using relationship:

A $\text{Average velocity} = \dfrac{\text{displacement}}{\text{total journey time}}$

B $\text{Average velocity} = \text{displacement} \times \text{total journey time}$

C $\text{Average velocity} = \dfrac{\text{total journey time}}{\text{displacement}}$

D $\text{Average velocity} = \dfrac{\text{total distance travelled}}{\text{total journey time}}$

E $\text{Average velocity} = \text{total journey time} \times \text{total distance travelled}$

2 The acceleration of a moving object can be calculated using the relationship:

A $\text{Acceleration} = \dfrac{\text{change in velocity}}{\text{time for change}}$

B $\text{Acceleration} = \text{displacement} \times \text{time}$

C $\text{Acceleration} = \dfrac{\text{time for change}}{\text{change in velocity}}$

D $\text{Acceleration} = \dfrac{\text{total distance travelled}}{\text{total journey time}}$

E $\text{Acceleration} = \text{change in velocity} \times \text{time for change}$

3 Which ONE of the following statements about speed and velocity is FALSE?

A Speed and velocity are both measured in m s^{-1}.

B Velocities must indicate a direction.

C Speeds and velocities never have the same size.

D Velocity indicates both the magnitude of the speed and the direction that an object travels away from a reference point.

E Objects can travel at different speeds to achieve the same average velocity.

4 A canal barge is travelling due east (090) with a speed of $1.5\,\text{m s}^{-1}$. A ball rolls with a speed of $3\,\text{m s}^{-1}$ due North straight across the deck of the barge.

The velocity of the ball as seen by an observer overlooking the canal is:
A   4.50 m s⁻¹ due east (090)
B   3.35 m s⁻¹ on a bearing of 063
C   1.50 m s⁻¹ due east (090)
D   11.25 m s⁻¹ on a bearing of 027
E   3.35 m s⁻¹ on a bearing of 027.

5 A light aircraft is flying due North (000) at 30 m s⁻¹. It is blown off course by a wind with a velocity of 20 m s⁻¹ blowing from the southwest (bearing 225).

Figure 44.3

The resultant velocity of the aircraft is:
A   46 m s⁻¹ on a bearing of 045
B   25 m s⁻¹ on a bearing of 113
C   46 m s⁻¹ on a bearing of 018
D   50 m s⁻¹ on a bearing of 225
E   21 m s⁻¹ on a bearing of 018.

6 Figure 44.4 shows a velocity versus time graph for a moving object.

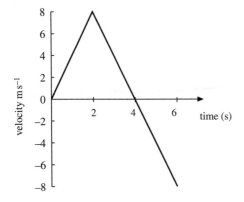

Figure 44.4

At which of the following times is the object moving at a speed of 4 ms⁻¹?
A   1 s and 3 s.
B   2 s and 4 s.
C   0 s, 4 s and 6 s.
D   1 s, 3 s and 5 s.
E   5 seconds only.

7 Figure 44.5 shows a velocity versus time graph for an object thrown upwards and rising for 4 seconds before falling back towards the starting point for 2 seconds.

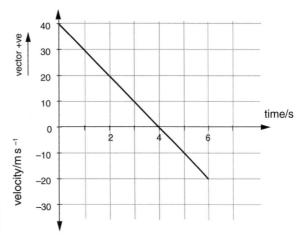

Figure 44.5

The maximum height reached by the ball thrown upwards is:
A   160 m
B   80 m
C   40 m
D   20 m
E   60 m.

8 A falling object accelerates from 5 m s⁻¹ to 25 m s⁻¹ in 2 seconds. The acceleration of the object is:
A   0.1 m s⁻²
B   0.3 m s⁻²
C   7.5 m s⁻²
D   10 m s⁻²
E   15 m s⁻².

9 A student uses the apparatus shown in Figure 44.6 to measure the acceleration of the trolley as it travels down a slope.

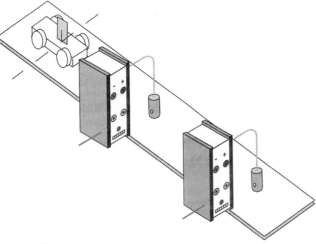

Figure 44.6

The student suggests that she has to measure the following quantities.

I   Interrupt times for the first and second light gate

II Time to travel between the light gates

III Length of the interrupt card.

Which of the above quantities must the student measure in order to calculate the acceleration?

A   III only.
B   I and II only.
C   I and III only.
D   II and III only.
E   I, II and III.

10 A car travelling at $27\,\mathrm{m\,s^{-1}}$ comes to a halt three seconds after the brakes are applied. The acceleration of the car as it comes to a halt is:

A $-0.11\,\mathrm{ms^{-2}}$
B $-3\,\mathrm{m\,s^{-2}}$
C $+3\,\mathrm{m\,s^{-2}}$
D $-9\,\mathrm{m\,s^{-2}}$
E $+9\,\mathrm{m\,s^{-2}}$.

11 Car X can accelerate from $6\,\mathrm{m\,s^{-1}}$ to $20\,\mathrm{m\,s^{-1}}$ in 7 seconds. Car Y can accelerate from rest to $18\,\mathrm{m\,s^{-1}}$ in 6 seconds. Which row in the table shows the accelerations of cars X and Y?

	Acceleration of Car X /$\mathrm{m\,s^{-2}}$	Acceleration of Car Y /$\mathrm{m\,s^{-2}}$
A	3	2
B	3.7	3
C	2	−3
D	2	3
E	3	3.7

MC3: Motion Graphs

1 The acceleration of a car starting from rest is shown in Figure 44.7.

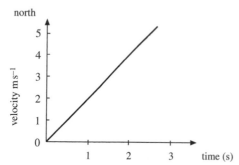

Figure 44.7

The car's speed after 2 seconds is:

A $2\,\mathrm{m\,s^{-1}}$.
B $4\,\mathrm{m\,s^{-1}}$.
C $6\,\mathrm{m\,s^{-1}}$
D $8\,\mathrm{m\,s^{-1}}$.
E $12\,\mathrm{m\,s^{-1}}$.

2 The velocity versus time graph for an object moving in a straight line on a level track is shown in Figure 44.8.

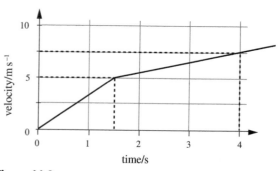

Figure 44.8

The distance travelled in the first 4 seconds of the motion is:

A 6.875 m.

B 10 m.

C 15 m.

D 16.25 m.

E 19.375 m.

3 The displacement of a moving object at different times is recorded in the following table.

Which of the following velocity time graphs could represent this motion?

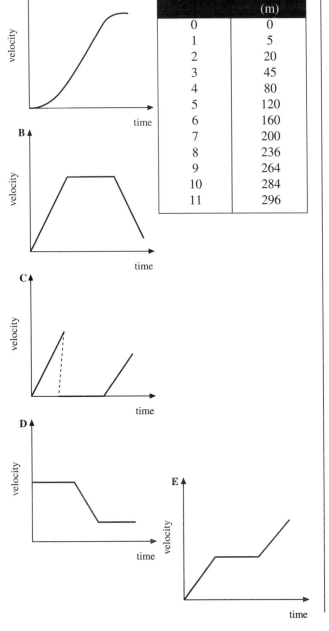

Time (s)	Displacement (m)
0	0
1	5
2	20
3	45
4	80
5	120
6	160
7	200
8	236
9	264
10	284
11	296

4 The velocity versus time graph of figure 44.9 represents the motion of an object being acted on by a constant force.

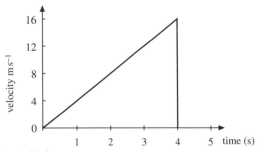

Figure 44.9

Which option shows the correct values for the instantaneous speed after 3 seconds and the average speed over the first 3 seconds of the motion?

	Instantaneous Speed	Average speed
A	$10\,\mathrm{m\,s^{-1}}$	$14\,\mathrm{m\,s^{-1}}$
B	$4\,\mathrm{m\,s^{-1}}$	$5.0\,\mathrm{m\,s^{-1}}$
C	$12\,\mathrm{m\,s^{-1}}$	$8.0\,\mathrm{m\,s^{-1}}$
D	$8\,\mathrm{m\,s^{-1}}$	$24\,\mathrm{m\,s^{-1}}$
E	$12\,\mathrm{m\,s^{-1}}$	$6\,\mathrm{m\,s^{-1}}$

5 In an experiment a ball, held directly underneath a motion sensor, is released.

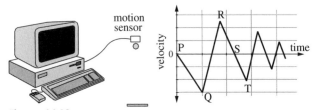

Figure 44.10

A pupil makes the following statements

I   At point P the ball is initially stationary underneath the motion sensor.

II Between R and S the ball is rising back towards the motion sensor.

III At point S the ball is stationary at the top of its first bounce.

Which of these statements is/are correct?

A III only.

B I and II only.

C I and III only.

D II and III only.

E I and II and III.

6 Figure 44.11 shows the acceleration time graphs for the motion of two Hot Rods in a dragster race. They are initially stationary and side by side.

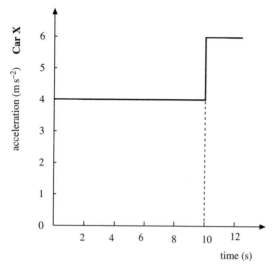

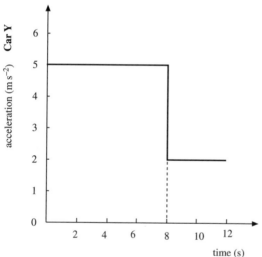

Figure 44.11

The following statements are made about the motion of the cars after 10 seconds.
I   Car X is travelling at $40\,\mathrm{m\,s^{-1}}$.
II Car Y is travelling at $44\,\mathrm{m\,s^{-1}}$.
III Car Y is in front of Car X.

Which of these statements is/are true?
A II only.
B III only.
C I and II only.
D I and III only.
E I and II and II.

7 A child's toy train travels on a track part of which is shown in Figure 44.12a. The child pushes and releases the toy at point P. The velocity time graph for the next 5 seconds of the motion is shown in Figure 44.12b.

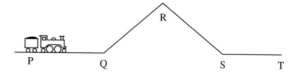

Figure 44.12a

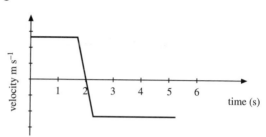

Figure 44.12b

After 4 seconds the car is:
A moving up QR and decelerating
B moving along ST at a steady speed
C moving down RS and accelerating
D moving back along QP at a steady speed
E moving down RS and accelerating.

8 The following velocity time graph represents the movement of an object in a straight line on a level track.

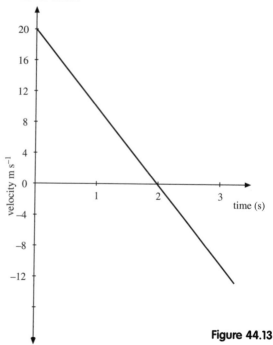

Figure 44.13

Which option shows correct values for the displacement and acceleration after the object has travelled for 3 seconds?

	Displacement (m)	Acceleration (m s^{-2})
A	718	212
B	6	212
C	18	210
D	14	210
E	14	212

MC4: Equations of Motion

1 A stone is dropped over the edge of a cliff. The height of the cliff is 78.4 m. How long does the stone take to fall to the foot of the cliff? (Use g = 9.8 m s^{-2}.)
A 3.3 s.
B 4 s.
C 5 s.
D 8 s.
E 16 s.

2 A car accelerates from 8 m s^{-1} to 32 m s^{-1} in 8 seconds. The acceleration is:
A 1 m s^{-2}
B 2.5 m s^{-2}
C 3 m s^{-2}
D 4 m s^{-2}
E 5 m s^{-2}.

3 While braking from 50 m s^{-1} to 10 m s^{-1} a train covers a distance of 600 m. The deceleration of the train is:
A 2 m s^{-2}
B 4 m s^{-2}
C 10 m s^{-2}
D 8 m s^{-2}
E 15 m s^{-2}.

4 A trolley is held at the top of a frictionless slope. The slope is inclined so that the trolley accelerates at 5 m s^{-2} down the slope. The time taken for the trolley to travel the first 2.5 m down the slope is:
A 1.00 s
B 1.41 s
C 2.25 s
D 2.50 s
E 5.0 s.

5 A stone is thrown vertically upwards in a region where the acceleration due to gravity is 10 m s^{-2}. The stone takes 3 seconds to return to the ground. The maximum height reached by the stone is
A 11.25 m
B 15 m
C 25 m
D 30 m
E 45 m.

6 A ball is dropped, from rest, from the top of a 45 m tall tower. Which row in the table shows the time taken to reach the ground and the average speed for the fall to the ground?

(You may assume that the acceleration due to gravity is 10 m s^{-2}.)

	Time to reach ground/s	Average speed during fall/ m s^{-1}
A	9	30
B	3	30
C	15	3
D	4.5	10
E	3	15

7 In the equation s = ut + 1/2 at^2 the term 'ut' represents:
A a speed
B an acceleration
C a displacement
D the initial acceleration
E an impulse.

8 A ball is thrown vertically upwards with an initial velocity of 50 m s^{-1}. It rises and falls unobstructed. How far above the release point is the ball 1 second **before** falling back to earth?

(You may make the approximation $g = 10\,\mathrm{m\,s^{-2}}$.)

A   10 m.
B   40 m.
C   45 m.
D   80 m.
E   120 m.

9   An object, fired vertically upwards, takes 16 seconds to return to the ground. Air resistance may be neglected. The initial speed of the object the object is:

A $10\,\mathrm{m\,s^{-1}}$
B $39.2\,\mathrm{m\,s^{-1}}$
C $78.4\,\mathrm{m\,s^{-1}}$
D $156.8\,\mathrm{m\,s^{-1}}$
E $240\,\mathrm{m\,s^{-1}}$.

10 In the summer, a stone is released from rest and takes 2.2 s to fall from the top to the bottom of an empty well. On a second occasion the stone takes only 0.8 s to reach the water in the well. How deep is the water in the well on this second occasion?

(You may make the approximation $g = 10\,\mathrm{m\,s^{-2}}$.)

A   3.2 m.
B   9.8 m.
C   21 m.
D   22.5 m.
E   24.2 m.

11 A helicopter is ascending with a steady speed of $10\,\mathrm{m\,s^{-1}}$. A small package is dropped from the helicopter. The package takes 5 seconds to reach the ground.

Which row shows the speed of the package just before it hits the ground and the height of the helicopter when the package was dropped?

(You may make the approximation $g = 10\,\mathrm{m\,s^{-2}}$.)

	speed/$\mathrm{m\,s^{-1}}$	height/m
A	75	50
B	50	160
C	40	75
D	50	75
E	40	80

12 A sprinter in a 100 m race starts from rest and accelerates uniformly for the first 6 seconds to reach a speed of $14.4\,\mathrm{m\,s^{-1}}$. He maintains this speed for the remainder of the race. What was his total time for the 100 m race?

A   9.94 s.
B   10.04 s.
C   11.90 s.
D   12.9 s.
E   13.41 s.

MC5: Projectiles

1   A small ball is kicked off the edge of a cliff. Which row in the table describes the horizontal and vertical components of the motion of the ball? Air resistance is neglected.

	Horizontal Motion	Vertical Motion
A	Constant velocity	Constant velocity
B	Uniform acceleration	Constant velocity
C	Uniform velocity	Uniform acceleration
D	Uniform acceleration	Uniform acceleration
E	Constant acceleration	Constant velocity

2   A ball is thrown horizontally with velocity of $10\,\mathrm{m\,s^{-1}}$ from the top of a 240 m tall tower. Approximately how long does it take for the ball to reach the ground?

A   7 s.
B   10 s.
C   14 s.
D   24 s.
E   49 s.

3   An aeroplane travelling horizontally with a speed of $60\,\mathrm{m\,s^{-1}}$ drops a package from a height of 122.5 m (as shown in Figure 44.14). The package has to land in the centre of a drop zone.

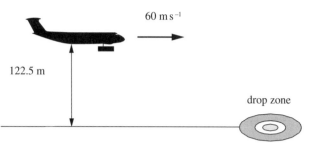

Figure 44.14

At what horizontal distance from the centre of the drop zone must the package be dropped from the aeroplane?

A 20.4 m.
B 60 m.
C 122.5 m.
D 300 m.
E 360 m.

4 A ball is projected with a horizontal velocity of 15 m s^{-1} from the edge of a table. Which of the following facts is/are used to calculate the horizontal distance travelled?

I The height of the table.
II The mass of the ball.
III The acceleration due to gravity.

A I and II.
B III only.
C I and III.
D II and III.
E I, II and III.

5 A small ball with very light line attached is fired with a horizontal speed of 30 m s^{-1} from a lighthouse towards a small boat in the sea. The height of the lighthouse is 31.25 m. How far from the bottom of the lighthouse will the ball land?

(You may make the approximation g = 10 m s^{-2}.)

A 30 m.
B 31.25 m.
C 53.6 m.
D 75 m.
E 191 m.

6 A ball with a light communications line is fired horizontally with a speed of 68 m s^{-1} from the deck of an oilrig towards a nearby support vessel (see Figure 44.15).

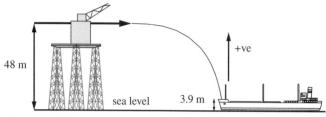

Figure 44.15

The deck of the support vessel is 5 m above the water and the rig is 49.1 m above sea level. The ball just lands on the rig. How far is the support vessel from the rig?

You may assume calm sea conditions and no air resistance.

A 44.1 m.
B 45 m.
C 54.1 m.
D 204 m.
E 215 m.

7 Using the apparatus shown Ball B is projected horizontally and leaves the launcher at exactly the same instant as Ball A is released.

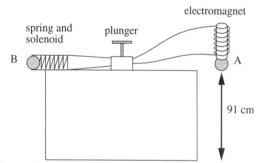

Figure 44.16

The balls have the same mass. Which of the following statements is TRUE?
A Ball A lands first.
B Ball A will land 0.81 s after being released.
C Ball A and ball B will hit the ground simultaneously.
D Ball A has a greater velocity than B just before reaching the ground.
E Ball B lands first.

8 A hot air balloon with a horizontal velocity of 4 m s^{-1} is flying at a height of 28 m. As the balloon passes over the start of a 10 m long outdoor swimming pool a bag of sand falls from the balloon.

Which of the following statements is/are true?
I The bag of sand falls for 2.39 seconds.
II The bag of sand will fall into the pool.
III A heavier bag would fall closer to the start of the swimming pool.

A I only
B II only.
C III only.
D I and II only.
E II and III only.

9 A marksman holding his cross bow horizontally, aims at a small ring attached to a tree 100 metres away. The bolt is fired with a speed of $250 \, \mathrm{m\,s^{-1}}$ from the cross bow. Which of the following statements is/are true?

I The bolt hits the tree more than 0.5 m below the centre of the ring.
II A lighter bolt would hit the tree closer to the ring than a heavier bolt.
III When the ring falls just as the bolt leaves the cross bow, the bolt hits the centre of the target.

A III only.
B I and II only.
C I and III only.
D II and III only.
E I,II and III.

MC6: Scalars and Vectors

1 Which of the following is a scalar quantity?
A Velocity.
B Acceleration.
C Force.
D Momentum.
E Kinetic Energy.

2 At the start of a yacht race one competitor travels 30 km north before being blown 3 km due south by a gale force wind. What is the resultant displacement of the yacht?
A 27 km North of the start.
B 30 km North of the start.
C 33 km North of the start.
D 27 km South of the start.
E 3 km South of the start.

3 A microlight aircraft is 75 m vertically above a marker point. This marker point is 180 m horizontally from a landing area. The distance from the aircraft to the landing area is:
A 75 m
B 133 m
C 187 m
D 195 m
E 255 m.

4 A pupil makes the following statements about vector and scalar quantities.

I Speed, time, distance and mass are all scalar quantities.
II Force, momentum and acceleration are all vector quantities.
III For motion in one direction in a straight line the magnitude of the velocity equals the speed.

Which of her statements is/are true?
A I only.
B II only
C I and II only.
D II and III only
E I, II and III.

5 In an orienteering event a girl runs North East (045) for 18 km then North West (315) for a further 5.25 km. Her final displacement from her starting point is:
A 18.75 km at 61.3° East of North (bearing 061.3)
B 23.25 km at 45° East of North (bearing 045)
C 18.75 km at 28.7° East of North (bearing 028.7)
D 17 km at 45° North of East (bearing 045)
E 12.5 km due North (bearing 000).

6 A trolley, of mass 2 kg, is at rest on a slope which is inclined at 60° to the horizontal. The component of the weight of the block acting **at right angles** to the slope has a magnitude of:

(You may make the approximation g = $10 \, \mathrm{m\,s^{-2}}$)

A 2 N
B 10 N
C 12 N
D 17 N
E 20 N.

7 A block of wood is released on a frictionless slope inclined at 30° to the horizontal. What is the acceleration of the block?

You may use the approximation g = $10\,\mathrm{m\,s^{-2}}$.
A $3.3\,\mathrm{m\,s^{-2}}$ down the slope.
B $5\,\mathrm{m\,s^{-2}}$ down the slope.
C $10\,\mathrm{m\,s^{-2}}$ down the slope.
D $5\,\mathrm{m\,s^{-2}}$ at right angles to the slope.
E $8\,\mathrm{m\,s^{-2}}$ at right angles to the slope.

8 A skier, of mass 69.4 kg, is travelling down a slope which is inclined at 35° to the horizontal. The size of the component of her weight acting parallel to the slope is:
A 390 N.
B 481 N.
C 557 N.
D 680 N.
E 694 N.

9 A block, of mass 3 kg, is pulled by a force of 20 N inclined at 30° to the horizontal. Which of the following forces would provide approximately the same horizontal acceleration?

A 30 N at 20° to horizontal.
B 10 N along the horizontal.
C 40 N at 25.6° to horizontal.
D 30 N at 54.7° to horizontal.
E 100 N at 85° to horizontal.

10 The following statements are made about the resultant of two forces **F** and **2F** which act on the same point as shown.

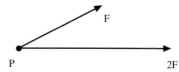

Figure 44.17

I The resultant force is less than $3F$ newtons.
II The resultant force acts in a direction closer to the 2F force than the F force.
III If point P was free to move it would move directly in the direction of the $2F$ Newton force.

Which of these statements is/are true?
A I only.
B II only.
C I and II only.
D II and III only.
E I, II and III.

(MC7/8) Newton's Laws

1 One Newton can be defined as the force required to:
A cause a 2 kg mass to accelerate at $2\,\mathrm{m\,s^{-2}}$
B lift a 10 kg mass through 1 m in 1 second
C lift an apple of mass 0.1 kg through 1 m
D lift an average sized apple through a height of 5 m
E cause a 2 kg mass to accelerate at $0.5\,\mathrm{m\,s^{-2}}$ along a frictionless surface.

2 A pupil suspends a mass of 5 kg from spring balance. The reading on the spring balance is:
A 5 N
B 44 N
C 45 N
D 49 N
E 50 N.

3 A force of 285 N acts on a block of mass 100 kg. The total frictional forces opposing the motion equal 135 N. The resulting acceleration of the block is:
A $0.67\,\mathrm{m\,s^{-2}}$
B $1.35\,\mathrm{m\,s^{-2}}$
C $1.50\,\mathrm{m\,s^{-2}}$
D $2.85\,\mathrm{m\,s^{-2}}$
E $4.20\,\mathrm{m\,s^{-2}}$.

4 A car of mass 250 kg accelerates from rest to $30\,\mathrm{m\,s^{-1}}$ in 6 seconds. The total forces opposing this motion equal 1500 N. The thrust produced by the car's engine is:
A 250 N
B 1250 N
C 1500 N
D 2750 N
E 3000 N

5 A motor scooter is travelling along a straight level road at a top speed of $25\,\mathrm{m\,s^{-1}}$. At this speed:
  A the thrust of the scooter engine just exceeds the frictional forces
  B the acceleration of the scooter is negative
  C the thrust of the scooter engine is just less than the total of the forces opposing the motion
  D the thrust of the scooter engine equals the total of the forces opposing the motion
  E the wind resistance will be equal to the force of friction at the wheels.

6 A cyclist is freewheeling along a level road. The cyclist now reaches an uphill section in the road. Which of the following statements describes the effect of this?
  A The bicycle will accelerate.
  B The bicycle will slow down because frictional forces will increase.
  C A component of the weight of the bicycle acts up the slope.
  D A component of the weight of the bicycle opposes the forward motion.
  E The bicycle will speed up as frictional forces will be less.

7 A car, of mass $250\,\mathrm{kg}$, accelerates from 0 to $30\,\mathrm{m\,s^{-1}}$ before the brakes are applied to bring the car to a halt in a further 6 seconds. The average braking force is:
  A $1250\,\mathrm{N}$
  B $1500\,\mathrm{N}$
  C $2450\,\mathrm{N}$
  D $2500\,\mathrm{N}$
  E $3750\,\mathrm{N}$.

8 When a skydiver jumps out of an aeroplane his vertical velocity changes in a manner shown in the following graph.

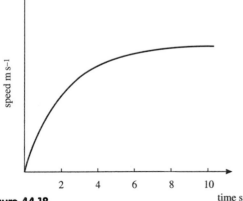

Figure 44.18

A pupil makes the following statements about this motion.
  I Initially the acceleration of the skydiver is $9.8\,\mathrm{m\,s^{-2}}$.
  II In the first 4 seconds speed of the skydiver and the forces opposing his movement are increasing.
  III After 8 seconds the skydiver is falling at his terminal velocity.

Which of the above statements is/are true?
  A III only.
  B I and II only.
  C I and III only.
  D II and III only.
  E I, II and III.

9 A trolley is travelling with a constant speed down an inclined runway. Which of the following statements about this situation is FALSE?
  A The forces along the runway are balanced.
  B Changing the angle of the incline causes an acceleration or deceleration.
  C Using a heavier trolley on the same incline with the same frictional forces produces a deceleration.
  D The acceleration of the trolley on a steeper slope cannot exceed $9.8\,\mathrm{m\,s^{-2}}$.
  E The component of the weight of the trolley that acts along the slope depends on the angle of the incline.

10 A rocket of mass $15{,}000\,\mathrm{kg}$ has an acceleration of $3\,\mathrm{m\,s^{-2}}$ from the launch pad. After 2 seconds the acceleration increases to $5\,\mathrm{m\,s^{-2}}$ although the thrust of the engines remains constant. Assuming that the gravitational field strength is $10\,\mathrm{N\,kg^{-1}}$ throughout the first 2 seconds the average fuel consumption of the rocket is:
  A $100\,\mathrm{kg\ s^{-1}}$
  B $500\,\mathrm{kg\ s^{-1}}$.
  C $1000\,\mathrm{kg\ s^{-1}}$.
  D $2000\,\mathrm{kg\ s^{-1}}$
  E $13{,}000\,\mathrm{kg\ s^{-1}}$.

11 A hot air balloon with a total mass of $200\,\mathrm{kg}$ is descending with an acceleration of $1\,\mathrm{m\,s^{-2}}$. A bag of sand with a mass of $20\,\mathrm{kg}$ is dropped from the balloon's basket. (You may assume that the acceleration due to gravity is $10\,\mathrm{m\,s^{-2}}$ and frictional forces are negligble.)

Which of the following describes the subsequent motion of the balloon? The balloon:

A stays at the same height

B continues to accelerate downwards

C begins to move upwards at a steady speed

D continues downwards at a constant speed

E continue with exactly the same motion as before.

12 A car is towing a caravan with speed of $25\,\mathrm{m\,s^{-1}}$ along a straight level road. The force of friction between the wheels of the caravan and the road is 2000 N. The frictional forces on the wheels of the car equal 5000 N. The tension in the tow bar between the car and the caravan is

A 0 N

B 2000 N

C 3000 N

D 5000 N

E 7000 N.

13 The velocity of a rocket when taking off changes with time as shown in the following sketch.

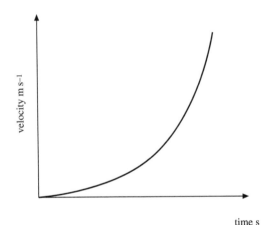

Figure 44.19

This can be explained by saying:

I the thrust remains constant while the mass decreases

II the unbalanced force on the rocket increases

III the rocket is accelerating uniformly.

Which of these statements is/are correct?

A III only.

B I and II only.

C I and III only.

D II and III only.

E I, II and III.

14 A rocket has a mass of $1 \times 10^5\,\mathrm{kg}$. The thrust required to give it an acceleration of $1\,\mathrm{m\,s^{-2}}$ from a launch pad is:

A 100 kN

B 880 kN

C 980 kN

D 1080 kN

E 1860 kN.

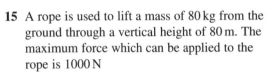

Figure 44.20

15 A rope is used to lift a mass of 80 kg from the ground through a vertical height of 80 m. The maximum force which can be applied to the rope is 1000 N

(You may use the approximation $g = 10\,\mathrm{m\,s^{-2}}$.)

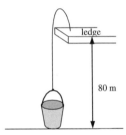

ledge

80 m

Figure 44.21

The shortest time in which this can be done is:

A 3.6 s

B 4 s

C 6.4 s

D 8 s

E 10 s.

16 A car of mass 300 kg is towing a caravan of mass 200 kg. They are accelerating at $4\,\mathrm{m\,s^{-2}}$. The frictional force on the wheels of the caravan is 500 N.

m = 500 kg

m = 800 kg

Figure 44.22

The force on the tow bar between the car and the caravan is:

A   700 N
B   1300 N
C   2000 N
D   1500 N
E   2500 N.

17 A mass of 1.35 kg is pulled along a level bench by a mass of 0.25 kg suspended over a pulley wheel as shown in the diagram.

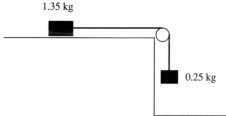

1.35 kg

0.25 kg

Figure 44.23

The total frictional forces acting are 0.45 N. The acceleration of the mass on the bench is:

A $1.25 \, \text{m s}^{-2}$
B $1.33 \, \text{m s}^{-2}$
C $1.48 \, \text{m s}^{-2}$
D $1.81 \, \text{m s}^{-2}$
E $8 \, \text{m s}^{-2}$.

18 A hot air balloon of mass 600 kg is floating at a steady height of 320 m. A bag of sand of mass 100 kg is dropped overboard.

Which row in the table shows the time for the bag of sand to reach the ground and the subsequent upward acceleration of the balloon?

(You may make the approximation $g = 10 \, \text{m s}^{-2}$.)

	Time to reach ground /s	Acceleration of balloon /m s^{-2}
A	8.1	2
B	6.4	12
C	8.1	10
D	6.4	2
E	8.1	1.67

MC9/10: Impulse and Momentum

1 A pupil makes the following statements about impulse.

I   It is the product of force and impact time.
II The impulse is numerically the same as the change in momentum.
III It is measured in N s^{-1}.

Which of these statements is/are true?

A   III only.
B   I and II only.
C   I and III only.
D   II and III only.
E   I, II and III.

2 The average force acting when a ball of mass 1 kg is accelerated from rest to $20 \, \text{m s}^{-1}$ by a contact lasting 10 milliseconds is:

A   2 N
B   20 N
C   2000 N
D   20 kN
E   200 kN.

3 In a sandblasting application a jet of air delivers $50 \, \text{kg s}^{-1}$ of small grains of sand horizontally onto a wall. The average speed of the sand particles is $20 \, \text{m s}^{-1}$. The sand particles fall vertically after the impact. The average force exerted on the wall during blasting is:

A   100 N
B   500 N
C   200 N
D   1000 N
E   2000 N.

4 Many modern cars have an automatically inflating air bag built into the steering wheel as a safety mechanism. The air bag inflates upon impact so that:

A   the momentum change in the collision is reduced
B   the driver's head is brought to rest more quickly
C   the driver's head slows down faster so momentum is lost more quickly
D   the deceleration of the driver's head is reduced
E   the momentum before the impact is less.

5 During which of the following collisions is the impacting force greatest?

A A mass of 10 kg brought to rest from $10\,\mathrm{m\,s^{-1}}$ in 1 millisecond.

B A mass of 1 kg travelling at $4\,\mathrm{m\,s^{-1}}$ returned along its original path at $3\,\mathrm{m\,s^{-1}}$ following a collision lasting 5 milliseconds.

C A car of mass 300 kg brought to rest from $10\,\mathrm{m\,s^{-1}}$ by a contact lasting 1 second.

D An elastic collision between a gas molecule of mass $5 \times 10^{-10}\,\mathrm{kg}$ travelling at $320\,\mathrm{m\,s^{-1}}$ hitting a wall for $1 \times 10^{-5}\,\mathrm{s}$ and returning along its original path.

E A mass of 10 kg brought to rest from $10\,\mathrm{m\,s^{-1}}$ in 1 second.

6 A pupil makes the following statements about momentum:

I It is a vector quantity.

II It is measured in units of $\mathrm{kg\,m\,s^{-2}}$.

III Momentum is not conserved when external forces act during a collision.

Which of these statements is/are correct?

A I only.
B III only.
C I and II only.
D I and III only.
E I and II and III.

7 When studying the bounce of a ball using the motion sensor a pupil records the following velocity time graph.

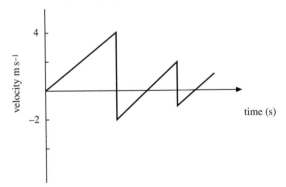

Figure 44.24

If the ball has a mass of 0.75 kg, the size of the change in momentum during the first bounce is:

A $0.75\,\mathrm{kg\,m\,s^{-1}}$
B $3.75\,\mathrm{kg\,m\,s^{-1}}$
C $4.125\,\mathrm{kg\,m\,s^{-1}}$
D $4.5\,\mathrm{kg\,m\,s^{-1}}$
E $8.25\,\mathrm{kg\,m\,s^{-1}}$.

8 In an air track experiment trolleys travelling towards each other as shown in figure 2 collide and stick together.

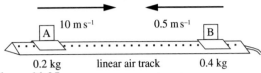

Figure 44.25

Their common velocity after the collision is:

A $0\,\mathrm{m\,s^{-1}}$
B $3\,\mathrm{m\,s^{-1}}$ to the right
C $3\,\mathrm{m\,s^{-1}}$ to the left
D $4\,\mathrm{m\,s^{-1}}$ to the right
E $4\,\mathrm{m\,s^{-1}}$ to the left.

9 Two trolleys of mass 1 kg and 0.8 kg, travelling towards each other on a linear air track collide head on. The 1 kg vehicle is initially travelling at $2\,\mathrm{m\,s^{-1}}$ towards the 0.8 kg vehicle which is travelling at $3\,\mathrm{m\,s^{-1}}$.

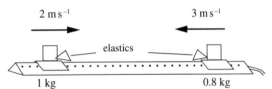

Figure 44.26

If, after the collision, the 1 kg vehicle returns along its original path at $0.5\,\mathrm{m\,s^{-1}}$, the 0.8 kg vehicle will have a velocity of:

A $0.125\,\mathrm{m\,s^{-1}}$ to left
B $0.125\,\mathrm{m\,s^{-1}}$ to right
C $0.5\,\mathrm{m\,s^{-1}}$ to left
D $0.5\,\mathrm{m\,s^{-1}}$ to right
E $5.375\,\mathrm{m\,s^{-1}}$ to right.

10 A cannon of mass 700 kg fires a cannonball of mass 1.5 kg horizontally to the right. The speed of the cannonball is $490\,\mathrm{m\,s^{-1}}$.

The recoil velocity of the cannon is:

A $0.95\,\mathrm{m\,s^{-1}}$ to the left
B $2.43\,\mathrm{m\,s^{-1}}$ to the left
C $1.05\,\mathrm{m\,s^{-1}}$ to the right
D $0.41\,\mathrm{m\,s^{-1}}$ to the right
E $1.05\,\mathrm{m\,s^{-1}}$ to the left.

11 In a cricket match the ball of mass 0.5 kg is bowled at a speed of $25\,\mathrm{m\,s^{-1}}$ towards a batsman. The batsman strikes the ball back along its original path with a speed of $30\,\mathrm{m\,s^{-1}}$.

The magnitude of the change in momentum of the ball is:

A $2.5\,\text{kg}\,\text{m}\,\text{s}^{-1}$
B $12.5\,\text{kg}\,\text{m}\,\text{s}^{-1}$
C $13.2\,\text{kg}\,\text{m}\,\text{s}^{-1}$
D $15\,\text{kg}\,\text{m}\,\text{s}^{-1}$.
E $27.5\,\text{kg}\,\text{m}\,\text{s}^{-1}$.

12 A steel ball with a mass of 0.2 kg falls from a height of 3.2 m onto a steel plate. The ball rebounds to a height of 0.8 m. The magnitude of the change in the momentum of the ball due to the contact with the plate is:

(You may use the approximation $g = 10\,\text{m}\,\text{s}^{-2}$.)

A $0.8\,\text{kg}\,\text{m}\,\text{s}^{-1}$
B $1.0\,\text{kg}\,\text{m}\,\text{s}^{-1}$
C $1.2\,\text{kg}\,\text{m}\,\text{s}^{-1}$
D $2.4\,\text{kg}\,\text{m}\,\text{s}^{-1}$
E $1.6\,\text{kg}\,\text{m}\,\text{s}^{-1}$.

13 A pupil is observing a trolley moving at a constant speed towards a barrier.

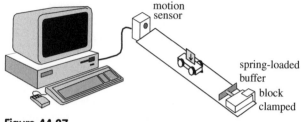

Figure 44.27

The bumper on the front of the trolley is spring loaded so the pupil makes the following statements:

I The total momentum before the collision equals the total momentum afterwards.
II During the collision the force from the trolley on the barrier is equal in size to the force from the barrier on the trolley.
III During the collision the force from the trolley on the barrier acts in the direction opposite to the force from the barrier on the trolley.

Which of these statements is/are correct?

A I only.
B III only.
C I and II only.
D I and III only.
E I and II and III.

MC11: Energy, Work and Power

1 The kinetic energy of an object of mass m moving with a velocity v is given by:

A $\frac{1}{2}mv^2$
B mv^2
C $\frac{1}{2}mv$
D mgv
E $\frac{1}{2}mgv$.

2 A pupil uses a motion sensor to record a velocity against time graph for a bouncing ball of mass 0.5 kg.

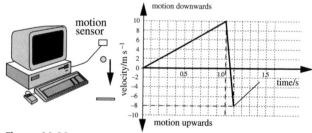

Figure 44.28

Approximately what percentage of the initial Kinetic energy is 'lost' during the first bounce?

A 36%.
B 44%.
C 50%.
D 56%.
E 64%.

3 A pendulum of mass m is raised through a vertical height h. The pendulum is released and its speed v through the lowest position of its swing is measured.

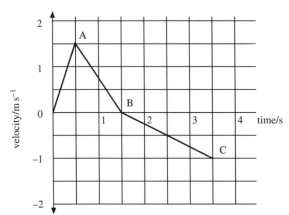

Figure 44.29

A pupil makes the following predictions.
I   Increasing h will increase v.
II Using a pendulum with a bigger m gives an increase in v.
III The velocity would be greater in a region where the gravitational field strength is greater.

Which of these statements is/are correct?
A I only.
B I and II only.
C I and III only.
D II and III only.
E I, II and III.

4 The unit of power is:
A J s
B W
C N s^{-1}
D kg m s^{-2}
E J s^{-2}.

5 The product of force and displacement is called:
A Impulse
B Momentum
C Acceleration
D Acceleration
E Work Done.

6 A car of mass 300 kg is brought to rest from a speed 50 m s^{-1}. The car travels a distance of 25 m while braking. The average braking force is:
A 300 N
B 3750 N
C 4050 N
D 15,000 N
E 30,000 N.

7 A lift of mass 100 kg carries 3 passengers of average mass 80 kg. The lift rises 5 m in a time of 49 seconds. The average power delivered is:
A 100 W
B 240 W
C 340 W
D 440 W
E 490 W.

8 A motor boat on a lake is travelling at a constant speed of 15 m s^{-1}. The frictional forces resisting the motion of the boat total 1500 N. Only 10% of the power from the engine of the boat drives the boat forward. The output power of the engine is:
A 100 W
B 1000 W
C 2250 W
D 22.5 kW
E 225 kW.

9 Which row in the table correctly compares the momentum an kinetic energy before and after an inelastic collision.

	Kinetic Energy	Momentum
A	no change	less after the collision
B	greater after the collision	no change
C	no change	no change
D	less after the collision	no change
E	less after the collision	greater after the collision

10 A tyre manufacturer is experimenting with a new combination of tyres and brakes. The following velocity against time graph is recorded for the motion of a test vehicle.

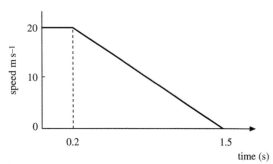

Figure 44.30

At time t = 0 the driver was told to apply his brakes. In analysing the graph an engineer makes the following statements.

I   The driver took 0.2 seconds to react to the instruction to stop.

II The car travels 17 m before stopping.

III The braking force was constant throughout the deceleration.

Which of these statements is/are correct?

A   III only.

B   I and II only.

C   I and III only.

D   II and III only.

E   I, II and III.

MC13/14: Density and Pressure

1 Which of the following gives the relationship between the density, mass and volume of a sample of material?

A   Density = ½mass × volume

B   Density = ½mass × volume^2

C   Density = $\dfrac{\text{volume}}{\text{mass}}$.

D   Density = $\dfrac{\text{mass}}{\text{volume}}$.

E   Density = mass^2 × volume.

2 The pressure (P) exerted by a force (F) acting on an area (A) is calculated using the relationship:

A $P = F \times A$

B $P = ½ F \times A$

C $P = \dfrac{F}{A}$

D $P = F \times A \times g$

E $P = \dfrac{A}{F}$.

3 When a metal bar is cooled it contracts. Which of the following is true?

A   The density and the mass decrease.

B   The density decreases and the mass stays constant.

C   The volume increases.

D   The density and the mass are unaltered.

E   The mass remains constant and the density increases.

4 A block of metal of density 1.9×10^4 kg m^{-3} has sides of length 5×10^{-2}m, 4×10^{-2}m and 10×10^{-2}m.

The block has a mass of:

A   0.01 kg

B   0.38 kg

C   0.95 kg

D   3.8 kg

E   380 kg.

5 In which of the following situations is there a pressure of 100 Pa?

A   A force of 100 N on an area 1 cm square.

B   A force of 0.1 N on an area 10 cm square.

C   A force of 0.01 N on an area 1 cm square.

D   A force of 1 N on an area of 1 mm square.

E   A force of 200 N on a rectangular area of 10 cm × 20 cm.

6 A cube of side 10 cm having a mass of 10 kg is placed on a smooth table. The pressure exerted by the cube on the table is:

A   0.98 Pa

B   1.02 Pa

C   1000 Pa

D   9800 Pa

E   10,000 Pa.

7 The lower side of the escape valve in a pressure cooker has an area of 1 mm^2. If the mass of the escape valve is 50 g what is the minimum pressure within the pressure cooker that will activate the escape valve?

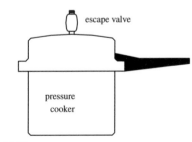

Figure 44.31

(You may use the approximation g = 10 N kg⁻¹.)
A   50 Pa.
B   500 Pa.
C   500 kPa.
D   0.5 Pa
E   0.5 kPa.

8   A block of metal of density 7.8 g cm⁻³ has sides
of 2 cm, 3 cm and 5 cm. It is placed with one of
its faces resting on a smooth table. What is the
maximum pressure exerted by this block on the
table?
A   39.0 Pa
B   23.4 Pa
C   58.5 Pa
D   1.53 kPa
E   3.82 kPa.

9   Milk expands when
it is cooled below
0 °C.

Figure 44.32

Which of the following statements is TRUE?
A   The mass of milk changes as it freezes.
B   The volume occupied by the frozen milk is
less than when it is in liquid form.

C   The mass of milk reduces and its density
increases.
D   The density of the milk decreases as it
freezes.
E   The volume of the milk decreases and its
density decreases.

10 The apparatus shown in Figure 33.33 is used to
determine the density of air. The flask is
weighed with the valve open and its mass is
recorded. 1000 cm³ of air is extracted from the
flask. The valve is closed and the flask is
weighed again.

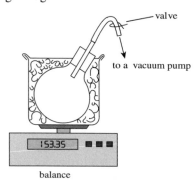

Figure 44.33

Mass of flask with valve open = 154.53 g
Mass of flask with valve shut = 153.35 g

The density of the air is:
A   1.20 × 10⁻³ kg m⁻³
B   1.20 × 10⁻² kg m⁻³
C   1.18 kg m⁻³
D   1.18 × 10¹ kg m⁻³
E   1.18 × 10³ kg m⁻³.

MC16: Gas Laws

1   A pupil is asked to complete the following
statement of Boyle's law by filling in the correct
words in the spaces W and X.

*'The pressure of a fixed mass of an ideal gas
kept at constant W is X proportional to the
volume.'*

Which row in the table shows the correct
choices for W and X?

	W	X
A	volume	directly
B	temperature	partly
C	volume	inversely
D	temperature	inversely
E	temperature	directly

2 A pupil is asked to complete the following statement of the second gas law by filling in the correct words in the spaces Y and Z.

'The pressure of a fixed mass of an ideal gas kept at constant Y is directly proportional to its temperature measured in Z.'

Which row in the table shows the correct choices for Y and Z?

	Y	Z
A	pressure	celsius
B	temperature	celsius
C	volume	kelvins
D	temperature	kelvins
E	volume	celsius

3 A pupil makes the following statements about the pressure exerted by a gas in a sealed container.
  I The pressure increases when the volume of the gas increases.
  II The pressure decreases as the temperature is reduced.
  III The pressure is caused by the molecules of the gas hitting the walls of the container.

Which of the above statements is/are correct?
  A III only.
  B I and II only.
  C I and III only
  D II and III only
  E I, II and III.

4 A pupil makes the following statements to compare the Celsius and Kelvin scales of temperature. Which statement is TRUE?
  A They measure different physical quantities.
  B A temperature rise of 10 K is less than a rise of 10 °C.
  C Doubling the Kelvin temperature will have more effect on the volume of a balloon filled with helium, than doubling the Celsius temp.
  D A temperature expressed in kelvin is numerically lower than the same temperature expressed in Celsius.
  E A temperature rise of 10 K is greater than a temperature rise of 10 °C.

5 The volume of a closed weather balloon is 15 m³ at ground level. At ground level the pressure is

1 atmosphere and the temperature is 7 °C. The balloon rises to a height of 1500 m where the temperature is 37 °C and the pressure is 80% of the initial pressure. The volume of the balloon is now:
  A 13.29 m³
  B 15 m³
  C 16.94 m³
  D 20.76 m³
  E 1500 m³.

6 The air in the 500 cm³ flask shown below is heated from 27 °C to 390 K before the source of heat is removed. Approximately how much water will go into the flask as the system cools back down to 27 °C?

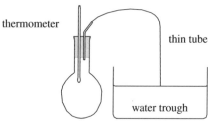

Figure 44.34

(You may assume that the connecting tubes are thin.)
  A 115 cm³
  B 150 cm³
  C 385 cm³
  D 500 cm³
  E 650 cm³.

7 An aerosol container has a volume of 200 cm³ and contains gas at a pressure of 2.525×10^5 Pa Atmospheric pressure has a value of 1.01×10^5 Pa. The nozzle on the can is pressed and held down until no more gas escapes. The volume of gas leaving the can is:
  A 80 cm³
  B 120 cm³
  C 200 cm³
  D 300 cm³
  E 500 cm³.

8 Which of the following statements about an ideal gas at absolute zero is FALSE?
  A The temperature will be approx −273 °C.
  B The gas particles will be at rest.
  C The gas will have a negligible volume.
  D The gas will exert a very high pressure.
  E The temperature will be 0 Kelvin.

9 A pupil makes the following statements about the molecules in a gas.
  I The collisions between molecules are inelastic.
  II When heated the gas molecules move more quickly.
  III Between collisions, the gas molecules move in random directions at constant velocities.

Which of these statements is/are true?
  A III only.
  B I and II only.
  C I and III only.
  D II and III only.
  E I, II and III.

MC17: Electric Fields

1 An initially uncharged polythene rod is rubbed with a woollen cloth. The polythene rod becomes negatively charged because:
  A electrons are transferred from the rod to the cloth
  B protons are transferred from the rod to the cloth
  C electrons are transferred to the rod from the cloth
  D protons are transferred to the rod from the cloth
  E equal numbers of electrons and protons are transferred from the cloth to the rod.

2 An initially uncharged polythene rod is rubbed with a woollen cloth. When the polythene rod becomes negatively charged:
  A the cloth also has an overall negative charge
  B there will be equal numbers of protons and electrons on the cloth
  C the cloth will have more electrons than protons
  D there will be no overall charge on the cloth
  E the cloth will have more protons than electrons.

3 An initially uncharged acetate is rubbed with a woollen cloth. The rod becomes positively charged because:
  A protons are transferred from the cloth to the rod
  B electrons are transferred from the rod to the cloth.
  C electrons are transferred to the rod from the cloth
  D protons are transferred to the cloth from the rod
  E equal numbers of electrons and protons are transferred from the cloth to the rod.

4 An initially uncharged acetate rod is rubbed with a woollen cloth. When the rod becomes positively charged:
  A the cloth also has an overall positive charge
  B the cloth will have more protons than electrons
  C there will be equal numbers of protons and electrons on the cloth
  D the cloth will have fewer protons than electrons
  E there will be no overall charge on the cloth.

5 Two straight parallel metal plates are placed 5 cm apart. One plate is connected to the positive terminal of a 5000 V power supply while the other is connected to the negative terminal of the same power supply.

A student writes down the following statements about this.
  I There is a potential difference of 10 kV between the plates.
  II The electric field between the plates is at right angles to the plates.
  III A diagram of the electric field between the plates should show equally spaced field lines.

Which of the above statements is/are correct?
  A III only.
  B I and II only.
  C I and III only.
  D II and III only.
  E I, II and III.

MC18: Current, Voltage and Resistance

1 There is a current of 20 mA in a lamp for 10 minutes. The charge, in coulombs, passing through the lamp in this time is:
  A   2
  B   12
  C   20
  D   200
  E   720.

2 In which of the following situations is the charge transferred greatest? A current of:
  A   25 A for 1 second
  B   10 A for 0.4 seconds
  C   0.25 A for 1 minute
  D   10 mA for 10 minutes
  E   1 mA for 1 hour.

3 A battery is rated as 0.5 ampere hours. This battery could be used in a circuit to supply a steady current of:
  A   2 A for 60 minutes
  B   0.5 A for 0.5 hours
  C   5 A for 10 minutes
  D   0.5 mA for 4 days
  E   1 A for 30 minutes.

4 A standard PP3 battery is described as having an output voltage of 9 V.

  This battery will supply:
  A   3 joules of energy to each coulomb of charge passing through the battery
  B   18 joules of energy to a circuit when there is current of 2 A for 3 minutes
  C   9 joules of energy to each coulomb of charge passing through the battery
  D   3 joules of energy to a circuit when there is a current of 3 A for 2 seconds
  E   9 kJ of energy to each coulomb of charge passing through the battery.

5 A 12 V car battery supplies a steady current of 200 A for 2.5 m s. The energy supplied by the battery is:
  A   3 J
  B   6 J
  C   62 J
  D   300 J
  E   6 kJ.

6 Two parallel metal plates are connected to a 5 kV power supply The work done by the electric field on an electron, charge -1.6×10^{-19} C, moving from the negative plate to the positive plate is:
  A 4.0×10^{-16} J
  B 8.0×10^{-16} J
  C 4.0×10^{-19} J
  D 8.0×10^{-19} J
  E 3.2×10^{-23} J.

7 Two parallel metal plates are connected to a 2.5 kV power supply. An electron, charge -1.6×10^{-19} C, is placed, then released, at the negatively charged plate. The kinetic energy of the electron just before it reaches the positively charged plate is
  A 4.0×10^{-16} J
  B 8.0×10^{-16} J
  C 4.0×10^{-19} J
  D 8.0×10^{-19} J
  E 3.2×10^{-23} J.

8 An electron, charge -1.6×10^{-19} C, is initially held at rest between two parallel metal plates connected to a 10 kV power supply. The maximum speed that the electron can have as it leaves the field is:

  (The mass of the electron is 9.1×10^{-31} kg.)
  A 1.85×10^7 m s^{-1}
  B 2.96×10^7 m s^{-1}
  C 4.19×10^7 m s^{-1}
  D 4.57×10^7 m s^{-1}.
  E 5.93×10^7 m s^{-1}

9 An LED, rated at 1.5 V and 7 mA, is connected in series with a resistor to a 5 V power supply. For the LED to operate at optimum conditions, the resistance of the series resistor is:
  A   150 Ω
  B   220 Ω
  C   500 Ω
  D   1.32 kΩ
  E   7 kΩ.

MC19: Series and Parallel Circuits

1 A student connects a 22 kΩ resistor and a 12 kΩ resistor in series with a 6 V battery. The battery has negligible internal resistance. She then connects an ammeter between the resistors in the circuit. The reading shown on the ammeter is:

  A 0.18 mA

  B 0.27 mA

  C 0.50 mA

  D 18 mA

  E 176 mA.

2 A student is asked to investigate the properties of a circuit where a 10 Ω resistor, 12 Ω variable resistor and an ammeter are connected in series with a 7.2 V battery. In deciding which type of ammeter to use she makes the following predictions:

  I The current in the circuit cannot be larger than 0.72 A.

  II As the variable resistor is altered from maximum to minimum resistance the ammeter reading changes from 0.33 A to 0.72 A.

  III The input resistance of the ammeter itself should be as high as possible.

Which of these statements is/are correct?

  A I only.

  B I and II only.

  C I and III only.

  D II and III only.

  E I, II and III.

3 Complete the statements below by adding the correct combination of words/phrases in positions X, Y and Z.

The current in a X circuit is Y Z at all points in the circuit.

	X	Y	Z
A	parallel	sometimes	the same
B	series	always	different
C	series	always	the same
D	parallel	always	the same
E	series	sometimes	different

4 Complete the statements below by adding the correct combination of words/phrases in positions P, Q and R.

The P of the potential differences across components in a Q circuit is R equal to the potential difference of the supply.

	P	Q	R
A	sum	parallel	always
B	difference	parallel	always
C	difference	series	sometimes
D	sum	series	always
E	sum	series	sometimes

5 You are given three resistors of values 10 kΩ, 22 kΩ, and 69 kΩ.

Which of the following resistor values cannot be made using these three resistors?

  A 6 kΩ.

  B 27 kΩ.

  C 31 kΩ.

  D 37 kΩ.

  E 101 kΩ.

6 Resistors with values 100 kΩ and 470 kΩ are connected in series with a 6 V battery. The battery has negligible internal resistance. The p.d across the 470 kΩ resistor is:

  A 1.05 V

  B 1.28 V

  C 1.62 V

  D 4.95 V

  E 6.00 V.

7 Resistors with values 220 kΩ and 470 kΩ are connected in parallel with a 6 V battery. The battery has negligible internal resistance. The current in the 220 kΩ resistor is:

  A 13 μA

  B 25 μA

  C 27 μA

  D 40 μA

  E 60 μA.

8 An electrical engineer connects a 56 kΩ resistor and a resistor of unknown resistance, labelled 'X', in parallel with a 12 V supply. The supply has negligible internal resistance. She measures the current in the 56 kΩ resistor as 214 μA. She finds that the total current taken from the battery is 814 μA.

Using these values she makes the following statements about resistor X.

I   The pd across resistor X is 12 V.
II The current in resistor X is 814 µA.
III Resistor X has a resistance of 20 kΩ.

Which of these statements is/are correct?
A II only.
B I and II only.
C I and III only.
D II and III only.
E I, II and III.

(MC20:) Voltage Dividers & Wheatstone Bridges

1 Two 10 kΩ resistors are connected in series with a 6 V battery of negligible internal resistance. The p.d. across each resistor is:

A 0 V
B 6.0 V
C 3.0 V
D 1.5 V
E 4.5 V.

2 Two resistors with resistance 10 kΩ and 20 kΩ are connected in series with a 9 V battery of negligible internal resistance. The p.d. across the 20 kΩ resistor is:

A 0 V
B 3.0 V
C 4.5 V
D 6.0 V
E 9.0 V.

3 A student, making revision notes about voltage dividers, writes down the following statements.

I   Voltage divider circuits have resistors joined in SERIES with a battery.
II The current in each of the series resistors is the same.
III The largest resistor will have the greatest p.d. across it.

Which of these statements is/are correct?
A III only.
B I and II only.
C I and III only.
D II and III only.
E I, II and III.

4 Two resistors with resistances of 56 kΩ and 69 kΩ are connected in series with a 20 V power supply to form a voltage divider circuit. The power supply has negligible internal resistance.

Which row in the following table shows correct values for the current in the 69 kΩ resistor and the p.d. across the 56 kΩ resistor?

	Current in the 69 kΩ resistor	p.d across the 56 kΩ resistor
A	0.29 mA	16.24 V
B	0.16 mA	11.04 V
C	0.29 mA	3.76 V
D	0.36 mA	11.04 V
E	0.16 mA	8.96 V

5 A pupil studying voltage dividers sets up the circuit shown in Figure 44.35.

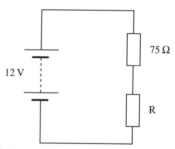

Figure 44.35

The p.d. across resistor R is 3 V. Which row in the following table shows the p.d. across the 75 kΩ resistor and the current in resistor R?

	P.d. across the 75 Ω resistor	Current in resistor R
A	3 V	0.04 A
B	3 V	0.16 A
C	12 V	0.16 A
D	9 V	0.12 A
E	9 V	0.16 A

6 A student making revision notes about Wheatstone Bridges writes down the following statements.

I A Wheatstone Bridge circuit has two voltage divider circuits connected in parallel to the same power supply.

II When the bridge is balanced the voltage at the mid point of each voltage divider is the same.

III When the bridge is balanced the current in each of the voltage dividers must be the same.

Which of these statements is/are correct?

A I only.

B I and II only.

C I and III only.

D II and III only.

E I, II and III.

7 A Student sets up the Wheatstone Bridge circuit shown in Figure 44.36.

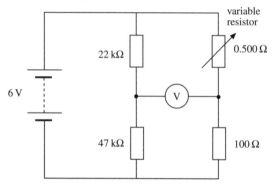

Figure 44.36

When the bridge is balanced the variable resistor has a value of:

A 47 kΩ

B 22 kΩ

C 213 Ω

D 47 Ω

E 10 Ω.

8 A second 100 Ω resistor is connected in parallel with the 100 Ω resistor in the circuit shown in Figure 44.36. The value of the variable resistor now needed to balance the bridge is:

A 23 Ω

B 94 Ω

C 107 Ω

D 427 Ω

E 147 Ω.

9 The Wheatstone bridge circuit shown in Figure 44.37 is **not** balanced.

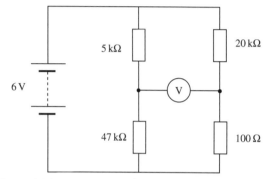

Figure 44.37

Which of the following changes will balance the bridge?

A Connecting a 10 kΩ resistor in parallel with the 10 kΩ resistor.

B Connecting a 20 kΩ resistor in series with the 20 kΩ resistor.

C Connecting a 67 kΩ resistor in parallel with the 100 kΩ resistor.

D Connecting three 10 kΩ resistors in series with the 5 kΩ resistor.

E Exchanging the positions of the 5 kΩ and 100 kΩ resistors.

MC21: EMF and Internal Resistance

1 A 3 Ω resistor is connected to a battery which has an e.m.f. of 10 V and an internal resistance of 1 Ω. The p.d. across the 3 Ω resistor is:
   A 2.5 V
   B 7.0 V
   C 7.5 V
   D 9.0 V
   E 10 V.

2 A digital voltmeter is connected across a 12 V battery which has an internal resistance of 0.8 Ω. The voltmeter has a very high resistance.

   Which one of the following statements is true?
   A When a 3 Ω resistor is connected across the battery the terminal potential difference, t.p.d., of the battery is 12 V.
   B The maximum output current from the battery is less than 12 A.
   C The e.m.f. of the battery is 12 V.
   D An ammeter would show a reading of 15 A when connected in series with the 12 V battery **and** the voltmeter
   E The reading shown on the voltmeter is less than 12 V.

3 A battery with an internal resistance of 0.7 Ω is connected in series with a 2.8 Ω resistor. The current in the circuit is 4 A and the p.d. across the 2.8 Ω resistor is 11.2 V. The e.m.f. of the battery is:
   A 2.8 V
   B 8.4 V
   C 11.2 V
   D 14 V
   E 22.4 V.

4 A battery with an internal resistance of 0.4 Ω is connected in series with a 3.9 Ω resistor. The p.d. across the resistor is 10.9 V. The e.m.f. of the battery is:
   A 1.1 V
   B 9.8 V
   C 10.9 V
   D 12 V
   E 106 V.

5 A battery of e.m.f. 4.8 V and internal resistance 0.2 Ω is connected across a 0 to 11 Ω variable resistor. The maximum current that the battery can supply is:
   A 0.43 A
   B 0.44 A
   C 0.96 A
   D 24 A
   E 53 A.

6 A very high resistance digital voltmeter connected across the terminals of a car battery shows a reading of 12 V. When the battery is tested by supplying current to a 0.5 Ω load resistor the reading on the voltmeter decreases to 11.2 V. The internal resistance of the battery is:
   A 0.022 Ω
   B 0.036 Ω
   C 5.6 Ω
   D 7.0 Ω
   E 22.4 Ω.

7 A student making notes about the circuit shown in Figure 44.38 writes down the following statements.

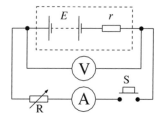

Figure 44.38

   I When the switch is open the reading on the voltmeter equals the e.m.f. of the battery.
   II When the switch is closed the reading on the voltmeter equals the t.p.d. of the battery.
   III When the switch is closed the reading on the voltmeter is greater than the reading when the switch is open.

   Which of these statements is/are correct?
   A III only.
   B I and II only.
   C I and III only.
   D II and III only.
   E I, II and III.

MC22: Electrical Energy and Power

1 An indicator lamp, rated 3.5 V and 250 mA, is connected to a 3.5 V battery. The battery has negligible internal resistance. The power dissipated in the lamp is:

  A 20 mW
  B 71 mW
  C 250 mW
  D 875 mW
  E 3063 mW.

2 A 50 W heater is connected across a 12 V power supply. The current in the heater is:

  A 0.24 A
  B 0.35 A
  C 2.88 A
  D 4.2 A
  E 21 A.

3 The p.d. across a 120 Ω resistor is 2.4 V. The power dissipated in this resistor is:

  A 20 mW
  B 48 mW
  C 50 mW
  D 200 mW
  E 690 mW.

4 An electrical appliance is rated at 700 W. Which of the following fuses would be most suitable for the plug used to connect this appliance to a 230 V supply?

  A 250 mA.
  B 0.5 A.
  C 1 A.
  D 3 A.
  E 5 A.

5 In which of the following situations is 1.8 MJ of energy transferred to other forms of energy?

  A A steady current of 250 mA from a 230 V supply for 90 seconds.
  B A 2 kW heater operating for 15 minutes.
  C An electric fire which uses 1 kW h of electricity.
  D A 50 W electrical heater operating for 1 minute.
  E A 2.5 A current from a 12 V battery for 1 minute.

6 Which of the following situations involves the largest transfer of electrical energy?

  A A 8 kW immersion heater switched on for 100 seconds.
  B A 700 W microwave oven operating for 5 minutes.
  C A 12 V battery supplying a current of 3 A for 2 minutes.
  D A 100 W lamp operating from 9pm to 8am.
  E A 70 W appliance operating for 10 hours.

7 There is current of 1.2 A in a resistor connected to a 20 V power supply. The supply has negligible internal resistance. The power dissipated in the resistor is:

  A 4 W
  B 14 W
  C 17 W
  D 24 W
  E 333 W.

8 A 12 V power supply with an internal resistance of 1 Ω is connected to a 4 Ω load resistor. The power dissipated in the load resistor is:

  A 9.6 W
  B 23 W
  C 36 W
  D 576 W
  E 720 W.

9 A data sheet states that a bulb is rated at 6 V, 250 mW. The current in the lamp when operated at its rated conditions is:

  A 7 mA
  B 15 mA
  C 24 mA
  D 42 mA
  E 1.5 A.

10 A 10 Ω resistor has a power rating of 2 W. The maximum current allowed in this resistor is:

  A 0.20 A
  B 0.45 A
  C 2.2 A
  D 4.5 A
  E 5.0 A.

MC23: AC and RMS Values

1 Which of the following describes the relationship between the r.m.s. voltage, V_{RMS} and its corresponding peak voltage, $V_{peak,}$ for a sinusoidally varying voltage?

A $V_{RMS} = V_{peak.}$
B $V_{peak} = V_{RMS}/\sqrt{2}.$
C $V_{rms}/V_{peak} = \sqrt{2}.$
D $V_{peak} \times V_{RMS} = 2.$
E $V_{peak} = V_{RMS} \times \sqrt{2}.$

2 An a.c. supply has a peak sinusoidal voltage of 14 V. This supply has an r.m.s. voltage of approximately:

A 7 V
B 9 V
C 10 V
D 20 V
E 28 V.

3 An a.c. power supply has an r.m.s. output voltage of 6 V. The peak value of the sinusoidal output is approximately:

A 3 V
B 4.3 V
C 6 V
D 8.5 V
E 12 V.

4 A 10 Ω resistor is connected to an a.c. power supply with a peak sinusoidal output voltage of 6 V. The power supply has negligible internal resistance. The maximum current in the resistor is:

A 0.42 A
B 0.60 A
C 0.85 A
D 2.36 A
E 4.72 A.

5 A student making revision notes about an a.c. power supplies writes down the following comments.

I The r.m.s. output of an a.c. power supply, with a sinusoidal output voltage, is always less than the peak output voltage.
II The r.m.s. output voltage of an a.c. power supply, with a sinusoidal output voltage, is approximately 71% of the peak value.
III A power supply with an r.m.s. output of 6 V

will deliver the same power to a load resistor as a d.c. power supply with a constant output of 6 V.

Which of these statements is/are correct?
A III only.
B I and II only.
C I and III only.
D II and III only.
E I, II and III.

6 Which of the following statements about the power from an a.c. supply, with a sinusoidally varying output, is true?

A The peak power is half the r.m.s. power.
B The peak power is $\sqrt{2}$ times the r.m.s power.
C The peak power is equal to the r.m.s. power.
D The peak power is twice the r.m.s. power.
E The peak power is 70% of the r.m.s. power.

7 A 4.7 Ω resistor is connected across the terminals of an a.c. power supply providing a peak sinusoidal output of 9 V. The supply has negligible internal resistance. The r.m.s. power dissipated in the resistor is:

A 1.9 W
B 8.6 W
C 17.2 W
D 42.3 W
E 190 W.

8 An engineer designs a circuit in which a resistor is connected to an a.c. power supply providing a peak output of 28 V. The current in the resistor is to have an r.m.s. value of 0.25 A. For safe operation the minimum power rating of the resistor should be:

A 2 W
B 4 W
C 5 W
D 7 W
E 10 W.

MC26/27: Inverting and Difference Amplifiers

1 A student making notes about inverting amplifier circuits writes the following statements.
  I The non-inverting input of the op-amp is connected to 0 V.
  II The output of the amplifier is connected to the inverting input of the op-amp by a resistor.
  III The input voltage of the amplifier is connected to a resistor joined to the inverting input of the op-amp.

  Which of these statements is/are correct?
  A III only.
  B I and II only.
  C I and III only.
  D II and III only.
  E I, II and III.

2 An inverting amplifier has a 100 kΩ feedback resistor and a 22 kΩ input resistor. The gain of this inverting amplifier is approximately:
  A −0.22
  B −0.35
  C −4.5
  D −59
  E −2200.

3 An inverting amplifier circuit has an output voltage of 2.5 V. The feedback resistor has a value of 100 kΩ and the input voltage is –1 V. The value of the input resistor is:
  A 2.5 kΩ
  B 40 kΩ
  C 100 kΩ
  D 250 kΩ
  E 400 kΩ.

4 An inverting amplifier circuit gives an output voltage of 10 mV. The input resistor has a value of 22 kΩ and the input voltage is −1 V. The value of the feedback resistor is:
  A 22 Ω
  B 220 Ω
  C 2.2 kΩ
  D 22 kΩ
  E 220 kΩ.

5 Which of the following statements correctly compares the input and output voltages for inverting amplifier circuits?

  A When the input voltage is positive the output voltage is positive.
  B The input and output voltages always have the same polarity.
  C The output voltage is always larger then the input voltage.
  D The input voltage is always larger than the output voltage.
  E When the input voltage is negative the output is positive.

6 A student sets up an inverting amplifier and notices that the amplifier is saturated. He suggests the following alterations to his circuit.
  I Decrease the size of the input voltage.
  II Increase the size of the input resistance.
  III Increase the voltage of the dual rail power supply connected to the amplifier.

  Which of these changes will eliminate the saturation?
  A III only.
  B I and II only.
  C I and III only.
  D II and III only.
  E I, II and III.

7 A student sets up a differential amplifier circuit with 4 identical resistors and two different input voltages.

  Which one of the following statements is correct?
  A The output voltage will always be 0 V.
  B The output voltage is the numerical difference between the two input voltages.
  C The output voltage is twice the sum of the input voltages.
  D The output voltage is twice the difference between the input voltages.
  E The output voltage is the sum of the input voltages.

(MC28:) Capacitance, Charge and p.d.

1 There is a constant current of 25 mA in a resistor for 3.1 minutes. The quantity of charge transferred is:
  A 4.53 C
  B 4.65 C
  C 4.75 C
  D 7.44 C
  E 7.75 C.

2 The current in an LED is 7 mA. The quantity of charge flowing through the LED in 1 hour is:
  A 0.07 C
  B 0.42 C
  C 0.7 C
  D 25.2 C
  E 252 C.

3 A photographic flashgun discharges 1.25 C of charge to produce a flash of light lasting 25 m s. The average current in the lamp of the flashgun during the discharge is:
  A 50 mA
  B 63 mA
  C 5 A
  D 20 A
  E 50 A.

4 A capacitor stores 11.75 mC of charge when the p.d across its plates is 25 V. The capacitance of the capacitor is:

  A 47 µF
  B 220 µF
  C 294 µF
  D 470 µF
  E 2200 µF.

5 A 2200 µF capacitor stores 264 mC of charge. The p.d across this capacitor is:
  A 8.3 V
  B 10 V
  C 12 V
  D 83 V
  E 120 V.

6 A constant current of 75 µA is used to charge a 470 µF capacitor for 125 seconds. What is the p.d across the capacitor at the end of this time?
  A 10 V.
  B 12 V.
  C 20 V.
  D 29 V.
  E 42 V.

7 A constant current of 50 µA is used to charge a capacitor for 3 minutes. The p.d across the capacitor at the end of this time is 6 V. The capacitance of the capacitor is:
  A 25 µF
  B 47 µF
  C 100 µF
  D 555 µF
  E 1500 µF.

(MC29/30:) Charging and Discharging Capacitors

1 A 100 µF capacitor is connected in series with a 20 kΩ resistor and an open switch to a 9 V battery. Which of the following statements is FALSE?
  A When the switch is closed the current in the circuit starts off low and then increases.
  B After the switch is closed the capacitor begins to charge.
  C After the switch is closed the p.d. across the capacitor increases.
  D The capacitor, when fully charged, stores 0.1 mC of charge.

  E Using a larger resistor would make the capacitor charge more slowly.

2 A 500 µF capacitor is connected in series with a 22 kΩ resistor and an open switch to a 9 V battery. When the switch is closed the initial current in the resistor is:
  A 22 mA
  B 0.41 A
  C 0.45 A
  D 1.8 A
  E 2.44 A.

3 A 1000 µF capacitor is connected in series with a 69 kΩ resistor and an open switch to a 10 V power supply of negligible internal resistance. At one instant after the switch is closed the p.d.

across the resistor is 3.85 V. What is the p.d. across the capacitor at this instant?

A 3.85 V.
B 6.15 V.
C 6.9 V.
D 8.35 V.
E 10 V.

4 A 2200 µF capacitor is connected in series with a 47 kΩ resistor and open switch to a 20 V power supply of negligible internal resistance. At one instant after the switch is closed the current in the resistor is 200 mA. The p.d.across the capacitor at this instant is:

A 9.4 V
B 10 V
C 10.6 V
D 11 V
E 20 V.

5 A 470 µF capacitor is connected in series with a 100 kΩ resistor and an open switch to a 18 V power supply of negligible internal resistance. At one instant after the switch is closed the current in the resistor is 35 µA. The quantity of charge stored by the capacitor at this instant is:

A 1.6 mC
B 3.5 mC
C 6.8 mC
D 8.5 mC
E 170 mC.

6 A 4700 µF capacitor, charged to 9 V is joined in series with a open switch and a 1.8 kΩ resistor. Which of the following statements is FALSE:

A When the switch is closed the p.d. across the capacitor decreases.
B The p.d. across the capacitor is always the same as the p.d. across the resistor.
C After the switch is closed the current decreases to 0 mA.
D A larger resistor would cause the capacitor to discharge faster.
E Before the switch is closed the capacitor stores 42.3 mC of charge.

7 A 1000 µF capacitor, charged to 15 V is connected in series with a 1.8 kΩ resistor and an open switch. The current at the instant the switch is closed is:

A 0 A
B 8.3 mA
C 67 mA

D 0.12 A
E 8.3 A.

8 A student connects a 100 kΩ variable resistor, open switch, ammeter and uncharged 220 µF capacitor in series with a 6 V battery. The battery has negligible internal resistance. She sets the variable resistor at its maximum value, closes the switch and the capacitor starts to charge. She makes the following observations about the charging process:

I   The initial charging current is 60 µA.
II By reducing the resistance in the circuit the charging current can be kept constant for a certain time.
III When the capacitor is fully charged the p.d across it is 6 V.

Which of these statements is/are correct?
A I only.
B I and II only.
C I and III only.
D II and III only.
E I, II and III.

MC32: Wave Characteristics

1 A student makes the following statements about waves.

I   A wave is a way of transferring energy.

II The amplitude of the wave determines the amount of energy transferred.

III The frequency of a wave is the same as the frequency of the source producing it.

Which of these statements is/are correct?

A   I only.

B   II only.

C   I and II only.

D   II and III only.

E   I, II and III.

2 Which of the following statements about waves is FALSE:

A   In a longitudinal wave passing through air the wave energy is transferred by the molecules moving to and fro along the direction in which the wave energy is moving.

B   In a transverse water wave the wave energy is transferred by the water molecules moving at right angles to the direction in which the wave is travelling.

C   Sound waves are not transverse waves.

D   Light waves are transverse.

E   Transverse waves always travel at $3 \times 10^8\,\mathrm{m\,s^{-1}}$.

3 The period of a wave is 50 m s. This wave has a frequency of:

A   2 Hz

B   5 Hz

C   20 Hz

D   20 kHz

E   50 Hz.

4 Circular waves spreading out in a ripple tank travel a distance of 20 cm in 2.5 seconds. The speed of the waves is:

A $0.05\,\mathrm{m\,s^{-1}}$

B $0.08\,\mathrm{m\,s^{-1}}$

C $8.0\,\mathrm{m\,s^{-1}}$

D $12.5\,\mathrm{m\,s^{-1}}$

E $50\,\mathrm{m\,s^{-1}}$.

5 A water wave of wavelength 0.05 m, travels 2 m in 8 seconds. This wave has a frequency of:

A   5 Hz

B   50 Hz

C   80 Hz

D   0.5 kHz

E   8 kHz.

6 Waves of frequency 3 kHz travel 165 m in 0.5 s. The wavelength of these waves is:

A   0.055 m

B   0.06 m

C   0.093 m

D   0.11 m

E   11 m.

7 A student writes down the following statements about reflection.

I   The angle of incidence always equals the angle of reflection.

II The angles of incidence and reflection are measured between the ray and the normal.

III The normal bisects the angle between the incident and reflected rays.

Which of these statements is/are correct?

A   I only.

B   II only.

C   I and II only.

D   II and III only.

E   I, II and III.

8 A student writes down the following statements about electromagnetic waves.

I   All electromagnetic waves are transverse.

II They all travel at $3 \times 10^8\,\mathrm{m\,s^{-1}}$ in a vacuum.

III Light and sound are both examples of electromagnetic waves.

Which of these statements is/are correct?

A   I only.

B   II only.

C   I and II only.

D   II and III only.

E   I and II and III.

9 A certain radio station uses a carrier wave of frequency 810 kHz. The waves from this station have a wavelength of:

A $2.70 \times 10^{-2}\,\mathrm{m}$

B $4.10 \times 10^{-1}\,\mathrm{m}$

C $3.70 \times 10^{2}\,\mathrm{m}$

D $1.50 \times 10^{3}\,\mathrm{m}$

E $2.45 \times 10^{3}\,\mathrm{m}$.

10 A source emits electromagnetic waves with a frequency is 2.5 GHz. These waves have a wavelength of:

A 8.30×10^{-1} m
B 1.20×10^{-1} m
C 8.30×10^{1} m
D 1.20×10^{2} m
E 1.20×10^{3} m.

MC33: Snell's Law, Internal reflection and Critical Angle

1 A student carries out an experiment on the refraction of light. He observes a ray of monochromatic light passing from air into glass. The angle of incidence of the ray is 29°.

He makes the following statements about the light.
I   The refracted angle is less than 29°.
II The light is travelling at 3×10^8 m s^{-1} before refraction.
III The speed of light in glass is less than 3×10^8 m s^{-1}.

Which of these statements is/are correct?
A I only.
B II only.
C I and II only.
D II and III only.
E I, II and III.

2 A ray of monochromatic light passes from air into glass as shown in Figure 44.39.

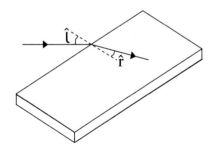

Figure 44.39

The angle of incidence in the air is 42° and the angle of refraction in the glass is 26°. The refractive index for the glass for this light is:
A 0.62
B 0.65
C 1.00
D 1.53
E 1.61.

3 A ray of monochromatic light emerges from a material at an angle of 39° to the normal. The material has a refractive index of 1.87. The angle of incidence in the material is:
A 19.7°
B 20.1°
C 24.6°
D 72.9°
E 90°.

4 Green light of wavelength 510 nm enters a material at an angle of incidence of 27°. The angle of refraction in the material is 20°. The wavelength of this in the material is:
A 378 nm
B 384 nm
C 510 nm
D 677 nm
E 688 nm.

5 A ray of blue light of wavelength 485nm enters a parallel sided glass block at an angle of incidence of 0°. Which of the following statements is FALSE?
A The angle of refraction in the glass block is 0°.
B The wavelength of the light is the same in the air and in the glass.
C The frequency of the light the same in the air and in the glass.
D The ray will emerge from the glass along a path parallel to the incident ray.
E The light will travel more slowly through the glass.

6 A ray of monochromatic light emerging from a parallel-sided block strikes the side at angles shown in Figure 44.40.

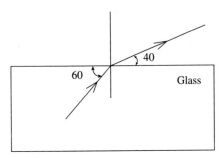

Figure 44.40

The refractive index of the material of parallel-sided block for this light is:

A 0.54
B 0.68
C 1.47
D 1.71
E 1.86.

7 In an optics exhibit at a science fair a ray of monochromatic light travels from X to Y through a block made from two different types of glass, P and Q as shown in Figure 44.41.

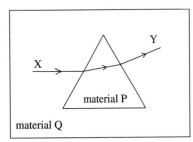

Figure 44.41

An observer makes the following statements.
I Materials P and Q have different refractive indices.
II Material P has a lower refractive index than material Q.
III The light is travelling faster in material P than in material Q.

Which of these statements is/are correct?
A I only.
B II only.
C I and II only.
D II and III only.
E I, II and III.

8 The partially completed ray diagram of Figure 44.42 shows three rays of monochromatic light emerging from a lamp placed 1 m beneath the surface of a pond of water. The refractive index of the water is 1.31.

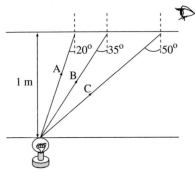

Figure 44.42

Which of the following statements is FALSE?
A Ray B emerges at an angle of 48.7°.
B Ray C is totally internally reflected.
C A circular patch of light will be observed when the pond is observed from above.
D The circular patch of light will have a diameter of 2 m.
E Removing some of the water from the pond will reduce the size of the circle observed on the surface of the pond.

MC29/30: Interference and Diffraction

1 A student uses the apparatus shown in Figure 44.43 to investigate interference.

Figure 44.43

Which of the following statements is FALSE?
A The meter shows that there is an interference maximum at point P.
B Moving the detector away from point P results in the reading shown on the meter reducing.
C Reducing the frequency of the microwave radiation produces a series of maximum and minimum readings on the meter at P.
D The gaps between the barriers act as separate sources of radiation.
E For the interference pattern to be set up the gaps between the barriers must be of equal size.

2 Two loudspeakers are connected to a signal generator as shown in Figure 44.44. The loudspeakers emit a sound of frequency 4000 Hz. The sound waves travel outwards through the air at a speed of 340 m s^{-1}.

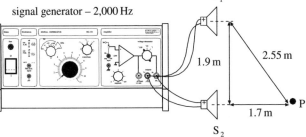

Figure 44.44

Which of the following statements is FALSE?
A The sound waves have a wavelength of 8.5 cm.
B The distance from S$_1$ to P is a whole number of wavelengths.
C The distance from S$_2$ to P is a whole number of wavelengths.

D Point P represents a minimum in the interference pattern.
E The waves arriving a point P are in phase.

3 Two sources are said to emit waves which are coherent when the waves from them:
A have the same frequency and a constant phase difference
B have frequencies which are very close to each other
C have the same amplitude
D interfere destructively at points equidistant from each source
E the same frequency and are in phase at all times.

4 Figure 44.45 shows straight waves approaching a gap in a barrier placed in a ripple tank.

Figure 44.45

Which of the following statements is TRUE?
A None of the waves pass through the gap.
B The waves emerging from the gap are perfectly circular.
C Making the gap narrower ensures that the emerging waves are straight.
D Some of the energy of the wave spreads into the geometrical shadow.
E The amplitude of the wave increases after the waves have passed through the gap.

5 Light from a laser is directed at a grating. The grating has 300 lines per millimetre and is placed between the laser and a screen. An interference pattern is produced on the screen.

Which of the following statements is FALSE?
A There are a number of bright and dark areas on the screen.
B Using a grating with more lines per mm would increase the separation of the bright patches.
C Using a laser emitting a longer wavelength of light would increase the separation of the bright patches on the screen.

D Moving the grating towards the laser
increases the separation of the bright patches
on the screen.

E Replacing a laser emitting red light with one
emitting green light reduces the separation of
the bright patches in the diffraction pattern.

6 Light from a laser is shone on to a grating
having 300 lines per millimetre. The light from
the grating produces a series of maxima and
minima of intensity on a screen. The second
order maximum of intensity is formed on the
screen at an angle of 23° from the straight
through position.

The wavelength of the light from the laser is:

A 3.26×10^{-9} m

B 6.51×10^{-9} m

C 8.83×10^{-9} m

D 1.30×10^{-6} m

E 6.60×10^{-4} m.

MC36: Irradiance and Photoelectric Effect

1 In which of the following situations is the
intensity of the radiation 1 **Wm**$^{-2}$?

A 100 Joules of energy arriving per second on
a area of 1 mm^2.

B 3600 joules of energy per minute arriving on
an area of 1 m^2.

C A power of 30 W on an area of 30 m^2.

D 100 joules of energy per second arriving on
a square of side 10 cm.

E A power of 10 W on a circle of diameter 1 cm.

2 The irradiance received from a point object:

A halves as the distance from the source
doubles

B increases as the distance from the source
increases

C increases as the time of observation
increases

D is 1% of what it would be at any point 10
times closer to the source

E is constant at all points along a line from the
point source.

3 At a point 2.1×10^9 m from a star the irradiance
is 1500 m^{-2}.

At a point 200,000 km **closer** to the star the
intensity is:

A 165 kWm^{-2}

B 1250 Wm^{-2}

C 1500 Wm^{-2}

D 1832 Wm^{-2}

E 6000 Wm^{-2}.

4 A student investigating the photoelectric effect
puts negative charges on the zinc plate of an
electroscope (shown in Figure 44.46).

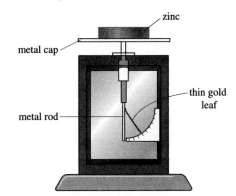

Figure 44.46

Light from a mercury discharge lamp is shone
onto the zinc plate. The student observes that
the leaf on the electroscope falls. The student
makes the following notes about her experiment.

I The leaf initially diverged because the
negative charges spread out evenly over the
rod and the leaf.

II Shining the light onto the leaf releases some
of the electrons from the surface of the zinc.

III Moving the light closer to the zinc makes the
leaf fall faster.

Which of these statements is/are correct?

A III only.

B I and II only.

C I and III only.

D II and III only.

E I, II and III.

5 A lamp emits monochromatic light with a wavelength of 254 nm. The energy of a photon of this light is:
A 1.68×10^{-16} J
B 7.83×10^{-19} J
C 8.70×10^{-36} J
D 2.61×10^{-27} J
E 1.68×10^{-40} J.

6 Photons with a frequency of 6.9×10^{14} Hz are shone onto a negatively charged platinum surface. The work function for platinum is 1.00×10^{-19} J.
A Photoelectrons will not be released.
B Photoelectrons will be released with kinetic energies up to but not exceeding 3.57×10^{-19} J.
C The photoelectrons released will all have an energy of 4.57×10^{-19} J.
D All of the released photoelectrons will have 1.00×10^{-19} J of kinetic energy.
E Some of the kinetic photoelectrons released will have kinetic energies above 3.57×10^{-19} J.

7 The threshold frequency for gold is 1.18×10^{15} Hz and that for sodium is 5.6×10^{14} Hz. Photons of energy 5.15×10^{-19} J will release photoelectrons from:
A a positively sodium surface but not a positively charged gold surface
B neither of these metals
C a negatively sodium surface but not a negatively charged gold surface
D negatively charged samples of both metals
E a negatively gold surface but not a negatively charged sodium surface.

MC37: Emission and Absorption Spectra

1 An atom with it electrons in their lowest possible energy levels is described as being:
A quantised
B in its ground state
C ionised
D in an excited state
E minimised.

2 Photons of light resulting from the transition labelled B in Figure 44.47 have a frequency:

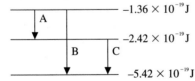

Figure 44.47

A of 8.17×10^{-14} Hz
B lower than those resulting from transitions A and C
C value of 6.12×10^{14} Hz
D higher than those from transition C but lower than A
E value of 5.42×10^{-19} Hz.

3 When an electron makes the transition from level O to level Q in Figure 44.48 the resulting photon has energy of:

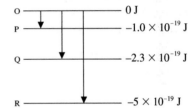

Figure 44.48

A 1.0×10^{-19} J
B 2.3×10^{-19} J
C 2.7×10^{-19} J
D 3.3×10^{-19} J
E 5.0×10^{-19} J.

4 A student is investigating spectra.

Figure 44.49

Using the apparatus shown in Figure 44.49 she puts the sodium pencil into the Bunsen flame in the gap between the sodium lamp and the screen. She notices that when the sodium pencil is placed in the flame a dark shadow is produced on the screen. She writes down the following statements about the experiment, which was carried out in a darkened room.

125

I There is no shadow, of the flame, on the screen before the pencil is put in the flame because light from the sodium lamp is falling on the screen.

II Burning the sodium produces excited sodium atoms in the flame.

III Some of the photons of the light from the sodium lamp are absorbed by the excited atoms and are prevented from reaching the screen.

Which of these statements is/are correct?

A II only.

B III only.

C I and II only.

D I and III only.

E I, II and III.

5 The absorption lines in the spectrum of sunlight led scientists to conclude that:

A not all frequencies of light are produced by the reaction at the core of the Sun

B some of the Sun's radiation is absorbed in the upper parts of the Earth's atmosphere

C the Sun radiates particular frequencies of light in specific directions

D elements in the layer of cooler gases around the Sun are absorb photons with certain energies

E some frequencies of light cannot pass through the space between the Sun and the Earth.

MC38/39: Lasers and semiconductors

1 When light from an LED is examined by a spectroscope it is found to be monochromatic. This LED emits:

A photons of several different colours

B light which is coherent

C a very intense beam of visible light

D only one particular frequency of light

E photoelectrons of only one wavelength.

2 Which of the following statements about n-type semiconductors is FALSE?

A The majority charge carriers are electrons.

B It could have been produced by doping silicon with an element from group 5 in the periodic table.

C Its resistance will be less than that of pure silicon.

D It can be combined with a p-type material to form a p-n junction diode.

E Their resistance is greater than that of the pure semiconductor used to form them.

3 A student making revision notes about semiconductors writes down the following statements.

I Pure silicon has a very high resistance.

II Adding arsenic (group 5) atoms to pure silicon reduces its resistance.

III Adding Indium (group 3) atoms to pure silicon increases its resistance.

Which of these statements is/are correct?

A II only.

B III only.

C I and II only.

D I and III only.

E I, II and III.

4 The wavelength of light emitted by a Helium-Neon Laser is 690 nm. The output power from the laser is 0.5 mW. The number of photons emitted by the laser each second is:

A 1.09×10^{-39}

B 4.32×10^{-19}

C 1.74×10^{15}

D 1.16×10^{19}

E 5.22×10^{22}.

5 A student making revision notes about lasers writes down the following statements.

I When radiation of energy hf is incident on an excited atom, the atom may be stimulated to emit its excess energy hf.

II In stimulated emission the incident radiation and the emitted radiation are in phase and travel in the same direction.

III The conditions in a laser are such that light gains more energy by stimulated emission than it loses by absorption.

Which of these statements is/are correct?

A II only.

B III only.

C I and II only.

D I and III only.

E I, II and III.

6 In the junction region of a forward biased p-n junction diode positive and negative charge carriers may recombine:
A by absorbing energy from the power supply
B to release photons with a continuous spectrum of energy
C by absorbing energy from the incident light
D and be emitted from the surface of the material
E to release photons with specific energies.

7 A student making revision notes about photodiodes writes down the following statements.

I In the photovoltaic mode a photodiode may be used to supply power to a load.
II The leakage current of a reverse biased photodiode is directly proportional to the intensity of the light incident.
III The switching action of a reverse biased photodiode is slow.

Which of these statements is/are correct?
A II only.
B III only.
C I and II only.
D I and III only.
E I, II and III.

(MC40/43) Nuclear Radiations and Half Life

1 Uranium has an atomic number of 92 and has isotopes with mass numbers 234, 235 and 238. Which of the following statements is FALSE?
A All of the isotopes have 92 protons.
B An atom of U-235 has 143 neutrons.
C The difference between U-238 and U-234 is one alpha particle.
D An atom of U-238 has three more electrons than an atom of U-235.
E U-238 has 4 more nucleons than U-234.

2 The diagram shown in Figure 44.50 describes how the number of protons and neutrons changes during a series of radioactive decays where element P decays into element T.

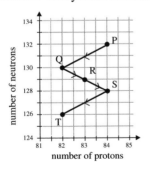

Figure 44.50

Which element has a mass number of 216?
A Element P.
B Element Q.
C Element R.
D Element S.
E Element T.

3 Figure 44.50 describes how the number of protons and neutrons changes during a series of radioactive decays. Which of the following changes represents the emission of a beta particle?
A P to Q.
B S to T.
C Q to S.
D Q to P.
E R to S.

4 In a fusion reaction Beryllium is bombarded with alpha particles of a certain energy. Carbon-13 is formed and gamma radiation is released. The masses of the nuclides involved in this reaction are as shown in this table.

Isotope	Atomic mass/ $\times 10^{-27}$ kg
$^{9}_{4}$ Be	14.9649
$^{4}_{2}$ He	6.6466
$^{13}_{6}$ C	21.5925

The maximum energy that could be released from 1g of beryllium such fusion reactions is:
A 1.71×10^{-12} J
B 1.14×10^{11} J
C 1.71×10^{12} J
D 6.68×10^{25} J
E 9.00×10^{13} J.

5 Which of the following statements is FALSE?
A Alpha particles produce a higher ionisation density than gamma Rays.

B Ionising radiations can be detected by a Geiger Muller tube.

C Ionising radiation can kill or damage the structure of living cells.

D Gamma rays produce a higher ionisation density than beta particles.

E Infrared is not an ionising radiation.

6 Which of the following statements is FALSE?

A The harm that ionising radiation can do to living cells depends on the exposure time.

B The harm that ionising radiation can do to living cells depends on the type of radiation used.

C The harm that ionising radiation can do to living cells depends on the mass of the tissue irradiated

D The harm that ionising radiation can do to living cells does not depend on the material between the source and the cells.

E The harm that radiation can do to living cells is minimised if the exposure time is kept as short as possible.

7 A student making notes about half-life writes down the following statements.

I The half-life of a substance is the time taken for half of the undecayed nuclei in the substance to decay.

II The half-life of a radioactive source is the time taken for the activity of the radioactive source to half.

III During the first 4 half-lives over 90% of the initially undecayed nuclei decay.

Which of these statements is/are correct?

A II only.

B I and II only.

C I and III only.

D II and III only.

E I and II and III.

Formulae

$$\text{Average speed} = \frac{\text{Total distance travelled}}{\text{Total journey time}}$$

$$\text{Average speed} = \frac{u + v}{2}$$

$$\text{Speed at light gate} = \frac{\text{Length of Card}}{\text{Time that light gate is interrupted}}$$

$$\text{Average Velocity} = \frac{\text{Displacement}}{\text{Total time for journey}}$$

$$\text{Acceleration} = \frac{v - u}{t}$$

$$\text{Uncertainty} = \frac{\text{Range of readings}}{\text{Number of readings}}$$

$$\text{Gradient} = \frac{\text{Change in } y\text{-axis variable}}{\text{Change in } x\text{-axis variable}}$$

$$v = u + at$$

$$s = ut + \frac{1}{2} at^2$$

$$v^2 = u^2 + 2as$$

$$F_{\text{H}} = F\cos \theta$$

$$F_{\text{V}} = F\sin \theta$$

$$F = ma$$

$$\text{Momentum} = \text{Mass} \times \text{Velocity}$$

$$Ft = mv - mu$$

$$m_1 u_1 + m_2 u_2 = m_1 v_1 + m_2 v_2$$

$$\text{K.E.} = \frac{1}{2} mv^2$$

$$\text{Work done} = F \times s$$

$$F \times s = \frac{1}{2} mv^2 - \frac{1}{2} mu^2$$

$$\text{Power} = \frac{\text{Energy transferred}}{\text{Time}} = \frac{\text{Work done}}{\text{Time}}$$

$$\text{\% Efficiency} = \frac{\text{Useful output energy}}{\text{Total energy input}} \times 100$$

$$\text{Weight} = mg$$

$$\text{P.E.} = mgh$$

$$E = mc\Delta T$$

$$E = ml$$

$$\text{Density} = \frac{m}{V}$$

$$\text{Pressure} = \frac{\text{Force}}{\text{Area}}$$

$$P = h\rho g$$

$$\text{Upthrust} = H\rho gA$$

$$P \propto \frac{1}{V}$$

$$V \propto T_{\text{ABS}}$$

$$P \propto T_{\text{ABS}}$$

$$T_{\text{K}} = T_{\text{°C}} + 273$$

$$\frac{P_1 V_1}{T_{k1}} = \frac{P_2 V_2}{T_{k2}}$$

$$I = \frac{Q}{t}$$

$$V = \frac{W}{Q}$$

$$R = \frac{V}{I}$$

$$R_{\text{T}} = R_1 + R_2 \ldots$$

$$\frac{1}{R_T} = \frac{1}{R_2} + \frac{1}{R_2} \cdots \qquad R_T = \frac{R_1 R_2}{R_1 + R_2}$$

$$V_X = \frac{R_2}{R_1 + R_2} \times V_S$$

$$\frac{R_1}{R_2} = \frac{R_3}{R_4}$$

$$P = V \times I \qquad P = I^2 R \qquad P = \frac{V^2}{R}$$

$$E = V_{tpd} + V_{lost}$$

$$I_{max} = \frac{E}{r}$$

$$V_{tpd} = E - Ir$$

$$V_{peak} = \sqrt{2} \times V_{rms}$$

$$\text{Frequency} = \frac{1}{\text{Period}}$$

$$\frac{V_s}{V_p} = \frac{N_s}{N_p} = \frac{I_p}{I_s}$$

$$V_{out} = -\frac{R_f}{R_{in}} \times V_{in}$$

$$G = \frac{V_{out}}{V_{in}}$$

$$V_{out} = \frac{R_f}{R_{in}} (V_2 - V_1)$$

$$Q = CV$$

$$E = \frac{1}{2} QV \qquad E = \frac{1}{2} CV^2 \qquad E = \frac{1}{2} \frac{Q^2}{C}$$

$$v = f\lambda$$

$$\hat{\imath} = \hat{r}$$

$$n = \frac{v_{air}}{v_{glass}} = \frac{\lambda_{air}}{\lambda_{glass}}$$

$$n = \frac{\sin \hat{\imath}}{\sin \hat{r}}$$

$$n_{1 \to 2} = \frac{1}{n_{2 \to 1}}$$

$$n = \frac{1}{\sin \hat{c}}$$

$$S_2 P - S_1 P = n\lambda$$

$$S_2 Q - S_1 Q = (n + \frac{1}{2}) \lambda$$

$$d\sin \theta = n\lambda$$

$$\text{Intensity} = \frac{\text{Power}}{\text{Area}}$$

$$I \propto \frac{1}{d^2}$$

$$E = hf$$

$$W = hf_0$$

$$hf = hf_0 + \frac{1}{2} mv^2$$

$$I = Nhf$$

$$W_2 = W_1 = hf$$

$$E = mc^2$$

$$\text{Average activity} = \frac{\text{Number of nuclei decayed}}{\text{Time}}$$

Corrected counts =
Counts from sample − Background counts

$$D = \frac{E}{m}$$

$$H = DQ$$

$$\dot{H} = \frac{H}{t}$$

Answers (numerical only)

Chapter 1: Distance, Displacement and Speed

1 b i $6.15\,\mathrm{m\,s^{-1}}$
  b ii 1 minute 50 seconds
  b iii greater, $6.36\,\mathrm{m\,s^{-1}}$
  c $6.25\,\mathrm{m\,s^{-1}}$

2 a $0.5\,\mathrm{s}$
  b $0.28\,\mathrm{s}$
  c $5\,\mathrm{m\,s^{-1}}$

3 a $20\,\mathrm{km}$
  b 106.7 litres

4 a $10\,\mathrm{m\,s^{-1}}$
  b $50\,\mathrm{m}$
  c $150\,\mathrm{m}$

5 B $6.83\,\mathrm{m\,s^{-1}}$

6 c $9.2\,\mathrm{m}$
  d $116\,\mathrm{m}$ North of starting point

7 a $6\,\mathrm{m}$
  b $5.55\,\mathrm{m}$ at $37°$ East of North
  c $0.6\,\mathrm{m\,s^{-1}}$
  d $0.56\,\mathrm{m\,s^{-1}}$ at $37°$ East of North

8 a $7.14\,\mathrm{m\,s^{-1}}$

9 a $130\,\mathrm{m}$
  b $130\,\mathrm{m}$ at $67.3°$ from vertical

Chapter 2: Velocity and Acceleration

1 d $8\,\mathrm{m\,s^{-2}}$
  e $-12\,\mathrm{m\,s^{-2}}$

2 a $4\,\mathrm{m\,s^{-2}}$
  b $7\,\mathrm{m\,s^{-1}}$
  c $24.5\,\mathrm{m}$

4 a $4\,\mathrm{m\,s^{-1}}$
  b $21\,\mathrm{m\,s^{-1}}$
  e $52.25\,\mathrm{m}$

5 a $1\,\mathrm{m\,s^{-1}}$
  b $1\,\mathrm{m\,s^{-1}}$ down runway

6 a $47.6\,\mathrm{m\,s^{-1}}$ on bearing 189
  b i $14.3\,\mathrm{km}$
  b ii $14.3\,\mathrm{km}$ bearing 189

7 $a_A = 6.8\,\mathrm{m\,s^{-2}}$
  $a_B = 5\,\mathrm{m\,s^{-2}}$

Chapter 3: Motion Graphs

1 a

Time/s	0	1	2	3	4	5	6
Velocity m/s	0	1.35	2.7	4	4.5	5	5.5

  b $1.33\,\mathrm{m\,s^{-1}}$
  c $0.5\,\mathrm{m\,s^{-2}}$
  d $14.25\,\mathrm{m}$
  f

Time/s	0	1	2	3	4	5	6
Displacement/m	0	0.65	2.6	6	10.15	15	20.25

2 a Both accelerations $= 1.67\,\mathrm{m\,s^{-2}}$
  c $8.36\,\mathrm{m\,s^{-1}}$

4 a Graph A
  b Table 1
    graph c
  c Table 3

Chapter 4: Equations of Motion

1 D

2 a $4.5\,\mathrm{s}$
  b $14.7\,\mathrm{m\,s^{-1}}$ upwards
  c $88.2\,\mathrm{m}$
  d $99.2\,\mathrm{m}$
  e $148\,\mathrm{m}$

3 a $4.9\,\mathrm{m}$
  b $67.1\,\mathrm{m}$
  c $23\,\mathrm{m}$
  d $36.3\,\mathrm{m\,s^{-1}}$ downwards

4 a $20\,\mathrm{m\,s^{-1}}$

b $20\,\mathrm{m\,s^{-1}}$
c i $14\,\mathrm{s}$
c ii $140\,\mathrm{m}$
c iii $10\,\mathrm{m\,s^{-1}}$

5 a $0.2\,\mathrm{m\,s^{-2}}$
b $0.57\,\mathrm{m\,s^{-1}}$
c $2.5\,\mathrm{m}$

Chapter 5: Projectile Motion

1 b i $0.4\,\mathrm{s}$
b ii $2\,\mathrm{m\,s^{-1}}$
b iii $0.8\,\mathrm{m}$

2 b $0.4\,\mathrm{s}$
c $0.88\,\mathrm{m}$
d $2.5\,\mathrm{m\,s^{-1}}$

3 a $2.2\,\mathrm{s}$
b $17.5\,\mathrm{m\,s^{-1}}$
c $27.5\,\mathrm{m}$

Chapter 6: Scalars and Vectors

2 a $5.5\,\mathrm{km}$
b $4.4\,\mathrm{km}$ at bearing 028
c i $7.3\,\mathrm{km\,h^{-1}}$
c ii $5.87\,\mathrm{km\,h^{-1}}$ on bearing 028

3 a $20.22\,\mathrm{km}$ on bearing 009
b $1.84\,\mathrm{km\,h^{-1}}$ bearing 009
c bearing 352

4 a $106\,\mathrm{N}$ at $19.3°$ to the $100\,\mathrm{N}$ force
b Resultant $= 146\,\mathrm{N}$ at $19.3°$ to $100\,\mathrm{N}$ force
c $146\,\mathrm{N}$ at $19.3°$ to $100\,\mathrm{N}$ force

5 a $409.6\,\mathrm{N}$
b $286.8\,\mathrm{N}$

6 a 086
b i $37.4\,\mathrm{m\,s^{-1}}$
b ii $37.4\,\mathrm{m\,s^{-1}}$ due east

7 a $16.3\,\mathrm{m\,s^{-1}}$ at $23°$ to vertical
b i 200 seconds
b ii $1300\,\mathrm{m}$

Chapter 7: Newton's Laws

3 a $60.2\,\mathrm{N}$ at $41.6°$ to horizontal
b $45\,\mathrm{N}$

6 a $47.5\,\mathrm{m\,s^{-2}}$
b $41\,\mathrm{kN}$
c $3.3\,\mathrm{kN}$
d 4.1 seconds

7 a $7.67\,\mathrm{m\,s^{-1}}$
b $2355\,\mathrm{N}$ upwards

Chapter 8: Newton 2

1 a $8.89\,\mathrm{m\,s^{-2}}$
b $6.4\,\mathrm{kN}$

2 b $0.15\,\mathrm{N}$
c i $0.70\,\mathrm{N}$

3 a $9.8, 9.8, 9.8$
b i $9.8\,\mathrm{m\,s^{-2}}$
b ii $14.7\,\mathrm{N}$

4 a deceleration $= 3.87\,\mathrm{m\,s^{-2}}$
b $25.32\,\mathrm{m}$
c $6966\,\mathrm{N}$

5 a $10.7\,\mathrm{kN}$
c $63.2\,\mathrm{kN}$
d i deceleration $= 0.25\,\mathrm{m\,s^{-2}}$
d ii $12\,\mathrm{s}$
d iii $51.3\,\mathrm{kN}$ Upwards

6 a $44.1\,\mathrm{kN}$
b $200,000\,\mathrm{N}$ (2 ropes side by side)
c $34.6\,\mathrm{m\,s^{-2}}$

Chapter 9: Impulse and Momentum

1 a $0.45\,\mathrm{Ns}$
b $0.45\,\mathrm{kg\,m\,s^{-1}}$
c $3\,\mathrm{m\,s^{-1}}$

2 a $2.5\,\mathrm{m\,s^{-2}}$
b $1850\,\mathrm{N}$
c $7400\,\mathrm{kg\,m\,s^{-1}}$

3 a $5000\,\mathrm{m\,s^{-2}}$
b $750\,\mathrm{N}$ in direction opposite to travel

4 a $800\,\mathrm{N}$

b 88 Ns
c $8\,\mathrm{kg\,m\,s}^{-1}$
d $13.66\,\mathrm{m\,s}^{-1}$

5 a $29\,\mathrm{m\,s}^{-1}$
b $36\,\mathrm{m\,s}^{-1}$

6 a $10\,\mathrm{m\,s}^{-1}$ downwards
b 5 m
c $3.5\,\mathrm{kg\,m\,s}^{-1}$ downwards
d $2.8\,\mathrm{kg\,m\,s}^{-1}$ upwards
e $6.3\,\mathrm{kg\,m\,s}^{-1}$
f 63 N

Chapter 10: Conservation of Momentum

1 a $1.6\,\mathrm{kg\,m\,s}^{-1}$
b $-1.2\,\mathrm{kg\,m\,s}^{-1}$
c $0.4\,\mathrm{m\,s}^{-1}$ to the right

2 b $0.0415\,\mathrm{kg\,m\,s}^{-1}$ to the right
c $0.0415\,\mathrm{kg\,m\,s}^{-1}$ to the left
d $0.024\,\mathrm{m\,s}^{-1}$ to the left

3 a $7 \times 10^5\,\mathrm{kg\,m\,s}^{-1}$
b i $1.7 \times 10^5\,\mathrm{kg\,m\,s}^{-1}$ (in original direction)
b ii $5.3 \times 10^5\,\mathrm{kg\,m\,s}^{-1}$ (in original direction)
b iii $88.3\,\mathrm{m\,s}^{-1}$ (in original direction)

4 a $3\,\mathrm{m\,s}^{-1}$
b $0.6\,\mathrm{kg\,m\,s}^{-1}$ downwards
d $1.1\,\mathrm{kg\,m\,s}^{-1}$ upwards

5 a $8750\,\mathrm{kg\,m\,s}^{-1}$
b $29.75\,\mathrm{kg\,m\,s}^{-1}$ to the right
c 29.75 Ns to the right
d 425 N

6 a $1.45\,\mathrm{kg\,m\,s}^{-1}$
b 6.3 Ns
c 6.3 Ns
d $53.4\,\mathrm{m\,s}^{-1}$

7 a 0.39 s
b iii $6.4\,\mathrm{m\,s}^{-1}$
b iv 69.6 N

Chapter 11: Energy, Work and Power

1 a 9500 J

2 a 13.2 kJ
b 52.7 W

3 a 0.098 J
c i $0.99\,\mathrm{m\,s}^{-1}$

4 a 4.86 J
b i $2\,\mathrm{m\,s}^{-1}$
b ii 1.9 J

6 a 7×10^5 J
b 7×10^5 J
c 2.8×10^4 N

8 a 3.12 J
b $2.44\,\mathrm{m\,s}^{-1}$

9 a 2750 N
b 8.25×10^4 J
c 1.1×10^6 J
d 5.5×10^3 W

Chapter 12: Weight and Mass

2 a 196 N
b 54 N
c $2.7\,\mathrm{m\,s}^{-2}$

3 b ii $1.4\,\mathrm{m\,s}^{-2}$
b iii $4.2\,\mathrm{m\,s}^{-1}$
c $0.6\,\mathrm{m\,s}^{-2}$
f (at end of journey lift is 29.6 m above starting point)

4 a 4.4×10^4 N
b 9000 N

5 a 490 N
b 3920 J
c 245 W

Chapter 13: Density and Pressure

1 a 744.8 N
b $4.8 \times 10^{-2}\,\mathrm{m}^2$
c 15.5 kPa

2 **a** 548.8 N
    b $480 \times 10^{-4} \, m^2$

3 **a** $1.2 \times 10^{-4} \, m^3$
    b $1005 \, kg \, m^{-3}$

4 **a** $7.85 \times 10^{-3} \, m^2$
    b **i** 31.8 kPa
    b **ii** 31.8 kPa
    b **iii** 1590 N

5 **a** $2.45 \times 10^3 \, N$
    b $12 \times 10^5 \, N$
    c $1.2 \times 10^6 \, N$

6 **b** $1.18 \, kg \, m^{-3}$

7 **a** 9173 N
    b $3.44 \times 10^5 \, Pa$

Chapter 14: Pressure in Liquids and Gases

1 **b** **i** 980 Pa
    b **ii** 102 kPa
    b **iii** $9.8 \times 10^{-4} \, N$ (only head of water pushes water out)

2 **a** 0.09%
    b 11.2 km

3 **a** $0.42 \, kg \, m^{-3}$

4 **a** 774 N
    b $1.15 \times 10^5 \, Pa$

Chapter 15: Flotation and Upthrust

1 **a** 9.8 N
    b 1.4 N
    c 1.4 N

2 **a** Z
    b Y

3 **a** $2.3 \times 10^{-3} \, m^3$
    b $2.3 \times 10^{-3} \, m^3$
    c 2.37 kg
    d 23.22 N
    e $2.48 \times 10^3 \, kg \, m^{-3}$

4 **a** 11.1 N
    b 2.45 N

    c 0.88 kg

5 **a** 10.1 N
    c 139 N

Chapter 16: Gas Laws

3 **a** $1.07 \, m^3$
    b $1.01 \, m^3$
    c 16 hours 40 minutes

4 **b** **i** $2.96 \times 10^5 \, Pa$
    b **ii** $5.92 \, cm^3$

5 **b** 400 K

Chapter 18: Current, Voltage and Resistance

1 **a** 300 C
    b **i** 6 J
    b **ii** 1800 J

2 **a** 1200 C
    b 7.5×10^{21}

3 **b** $2.4 \times 10^{-16} \, J$
    c $2.4 \times 10^{-16} \, J$
    d $2.3 \times 10^7 \, m \, s^{-1}$

5 **d** $4.9 \, \Omega$

6 **a** 5 mA
    b 1.5 V
    c 7.5 V

Chapter 19: Series and Parallel Circuits

1 **a** 0.25 A
    c 9 V

2 **a** 1.5 V
    b 4.5 V
    c $225 \, \Omega$
    d $300 \, \Omega$
    e $A_1 = 0.107 \, A$
       $A_2 = 0.080 \, A$
       $A_3 = 0.027 \, A$

4 **b** 47 kΩ

5 **b** **i** 59 mA

b ii 52 mA
b iii 111 mA
c i 1.8 V
c ii 1 V
c iii 2.8 V

Chapter 20: Voltage Dividers and Wheatstone Bridges

1 **a** 69 Ω
  c 4.09 V

3 **a** 6 V
  b 80 mA
  d iii 60 mA

4 **b** 56.4 kΩ

5 **c** i 88 Ω
  c ii 22 kΩ

Chapter 21: e.m.f and Internal Resistance

3 **a** 1.33 A
  b 0.66 V

4 **a** 24 V
  b 44 A

5 **a** 6 V
  b 1.2 Ω
  c 5 A

6 **b** i 9 V
  b ii 6 A
  c 1.5 Ω
  d 12, 12.6, 13.2, 13.5, 12.96, 10.12

Chapter 22: Electrical Energy and Power

2 **a** 5.5 V
  c 1.375 W
  d 8.75 J

3 **b** 13 A
  c i 39 A

4 **b** 8 W

c 100 J
d 180 J

5 **b** 0.67 A
  e 65%

Chapter 23: A.C. and R.M.S. Values

1 **b** 9.9 V

2 **a** 8.49 V

3 **a** 6.4 mA
  b 40 mW
  c i 500 Ω
  c ii 12.8 mA
  d 6.36 V

4 **c** i 8.49 V
  c iii 1.78 W
  c iv 0.89 W

Chapter 24: Sensors, Transistors and Basic Electronics

2 **a** 3 V
  b 2 V
  c 200 Ω

Chapter 25: Inverting Amplifiers – Basic Circuits

2 **c** 1.45 V
  e i 66 µA
  e iii 3.1

3 **a** 2.1
  b i 50 Hz

4 **b** −15 V
  c 40 kΩ

Chapter 26: Inverting Amplifiers 2

1 **b** − 16
 c − 0.75 V
 d − 0.075 V
 e i + 0.075 V

2 **a** − 2.2
 b − 3.3 V

3 **b** −3.71 V
 c 8.09 V, 12.14 V, 15 V, −15 V

4 **a** 0.7 V
 d 3.1 V
 e −3.1 V

5 **b** −14.6 V

Chapter 27: Difference Amplifiers

2 **b** 39.3 kΩ
 c i 1.8 V
 c ii 14 V

Chapter 28: Capacitance, Charge and Potential Difference

2 **a** 0.36 C
 b 167 s

3 **b** 423 mC
 c 745 V

4 **a** 37.5 A
 b 0.01 F

5 **b** i 3.9 V
 c 476 μF
 d 5.4 V

6 **a** 1080 μC
 b 72 μF
 c 1.8 mC

Chapter 29: Charging Capacitors

1 **b** 5.8 V
 e i 3 V
 e ii 6 V

2 **f** 14.9 μA

3 **b** 9 V
 c 9 V, 5.71 V, 3.63 V, 2.30 V, 1.46 V, 0.93 V.
 d 90 μA, 57.1 μA, 36.3 μA, 23 μA, 14.6 μA, 9.3 μA

Chapter 30: Discharging Capacitors

1 **b** 4.2 V
 c 4.8×10^{-4} C

3 **c** 0.55, 0.34, 0.21, 0.13, 0.08, 0.05

4 **a** 1.98 mC
 b 9 V
 c 19 μA
 d i 2.82 V

Chapter 31: Capacitors and Energy

2 **a** 2 A
 b 4 mF
 c 31.25 J
 d 125 W

4 **a** 100 μF
 d $E_x = 1.8$ mJ, $E_y = 7.2$ mJ

5 **c** 440 μC
 e 1.83 mJ

6 **a** 2 J
 b 0.72 J
 c 1.28 J

Chapter 32: Wave Characteristics

1 **a** 495 m
 b 3.4×10^{-3} s

c 1.14 m

6 a 471 Hz
  b 235
  c 165 m

7 a 0.2 s
  b 150 m

9 836 m

Chapter 33: Snell's Law, Internal Reflection and Critical angle

2 b 30°

3 a 640 nm
  b 1.46
  d 438 nm

5 b 378 nm

7 b 47.8°

8 b $1.91 \times 10^8 \, \text{m s}^{-1}$
  c $2.1 \times 10^8 \, \text{m s}^{-1}$

9 a $1.98 \ 3 \ 10^8 \, \text{m s}^{-1}$
  b $2.1 \times 10^8 \, \text{m s}^{-1}$
  c 34.8°
  d 34.3°
10 a 1.21
  b 55.7°

Chapter 34: Interference

4 b 5 cm

6 b 2 cm
  c i 30 cm
  c ii 35 cm

Chapter 35: Diffraction

4 c 39.8°
  d 3.33 m

Chapter 36: Irradiance and Photoelectric Effect

3 a $1605 \, \text{Wm}^{-2}$
  c $3595 \, \text{Wm}^{-2}$

5 a $7.8 \times 10^{-19} \, \text{J}$
  c 2.5×10^{13}
  d 19.5 mJ
  e $21.7 \, \text{m Wm}^{-2}$

6 a $7.8 \ 3 \ 10^{-19} \, \text{J}$
  b $6.4 \times 10^{-19} \, \text{J}$
  c $1.4 \times 10^{-19} \, \text{J}$
  d $6.41 \times 10^{-19} \, \text{J}$

Chapter 37: Emission and Absorption Spectra

2 b $3 \times 10^{-19} \, \text{J}$
  c $2.47 \times 10^{15} \, \text{Hz}$

5 a $2.43 \times 10^{-19} \, \text{J}$
  b 817 nm
  c X = 436 nm
    Y = 546 nm
    Z = 583 nm

6 b $2.37 \times 10^{-19} \, \text{J}$

Chapter 38: Lasers and Semiconductors

5 b i $4.08 \times 10^{-19} \, \text{J}$
  b ii 4.9×10^{18}
  b iii 4.9×10^{20}
  c $1.13 \times 10^6 \, \text{Wm}^{-2}$

Chapter 39: p-n Junctions and Photodiodes

4 a I 250 Hz

5 b I 509 nm
  b iii $3.9 \times 10^{-19} \, \text{J}$

Chapter 40: Nuclear Changes

2 a 92
e 142, 143, 146

3 c 144

6 a 1 proton, 0 neutrons
b 0 protons, 1 neutron

7 a $x = 30$, $y = 15$

Chapter 41: Fission and Fusion

3 c 7.37×10^{13} J

Chapter 42: Radiation and Matter

3 c i 12.5 Gy

4 a 4.32 mJ

5 b 42.3 m Sv

6 (In this question the activity of the alpha source should be 20 kBq and not as shown in fig 42.3)
a 20,000
c $0.3 \, \mu \, Svs^{-1}$
d 2.2×10^{-5} J

Chapter 43: Half Life and Half Value Thickness

2 b 1/64
c 140 s

5 a 160 counts/minute above background.

Chapter 44

MC 1: Distance, Displacement and Speed

Question	Answer
1	A
2	D
3	D
4	C
5	B
6	B
7	E
8	E

MC 2: Velocity and Acceleration

Question	Answer
1	A
2	A
3	C
4	E
5	C
6	D
7	B
8	D
9	E
10	D
11	D

MC 3: Motion Graphs

Question	Answer
1	B
2	E
3	B
4	E
5	E
6	E
7	D
8	E

MC 4: Equations of Motion

Question	Answer
1	B
2	C
3	A
4	A
5	A
6	E
7	C
8	C
9	C
10	C
11	C
12	A

MC 5: Projectiles

Question	Answer
1	C
2	A
3	D
4	C
5	D
6	D
7	C
8	D
9	C

MC 6: Scalars and Vectors

Question	Answer
1	E
2	A
3	D
4	E
5	C
6	B
7	B
8	A
9	D
10	C

MC7/8: Newton's Laws

Question	Answer
1	E
2	D
3	C
4	D
5	D
6	D
7	A
8	E
9	C
10	C
11	D
12	B
13	B
14	D
15	D
16	B
17	A
18	A

MC 9/10: Impulse and Momentum

Question	Answer
1	B
2	C
3	D
4	D
5	A
6	D
7	D
8	B
9	B
10	E
11	E
12	D
13	E

MC 11: Energy, Work and Power

Question	Answer
1	A
2	A
3	C
4	B
5	E
6	D
7	C
8	E
9	D
10	E

MC 13/14: Density and Pressure

Question	Answer
1	D
2	C
3	E
4	D
5	C
6	D
7	C
8	E
9	D
10	C

MC 16: Gas Laws

Question	Answer
1	D
2	C
3	D
4	C
5	D
6	B
7	D
8	D
9	D

MC 17: Electric Fields

Question	Answer
1	C
2	E
3	B
4	D
5	D

MC 18: Current, Voltage and Resistance

Question	Answer
1	B
2	A
3	E
4	C
5	B
6	B
7	E
8	E
9	C

MC 19: Series And Parallel Circuits

Question	Answer
1	A
2	B
3	C
4	D
5	D
6	D
7	C
8	C

MC 20: Voltage Dividers and Wheatstone Bridges

Question	Answer
1	C
2	D
3	E
4	E
5	D
6	B
7	D
8	A
9	C

MC 21: emf and Internal Resistance

Question	Answer
1	C
2	C
3	D
4	D
5	D
6	B
7	B

MC 22: Electrical Energy and Power

Question	Answer
1	D
2	D
3	B
4	D
5	B
6	D
7	D
8	B
9	D
10	B

MC23: A.C. and R.M.S. values

Question	Answer
1	E
2	C
3	D
4	B
5	E
6	D
7	B
8	E

MC26/27: Inverting and Difference Amplifiers

Question	Answer
1	E
2	C
3	B
4	B
5	E
6	E
7	B

MC 28: Capacitance, Charge and Potential Difference

Question	Answer
1	B
2	D
3	E
4	D
5	E
6	C
7	E

MC29/30: Charging and Discharging Capacitors

Question	Answer
1	A
2	B
3	B
4	C
5	C
6	D
7	B
8	E

MC 32: Wave Properties

Question	Answer
1	E
2	E
3	C
4	B
5	A
6	D
7	E
8	C
9	C
10	B

MC 33: Snell's Law

Question	Answer
1	E
2	D
3	A
4	B
5	B
6	E
7	E
8	D

MC 34/35: Interference and Diffraction

Question	Answer
1	C
2	D
3	A
4	D
5	E
6	B

MC 36: Radiation Intensity and Photoelectric Effect

Question	Answer
1	D
2	D
3	D
4	E
5	B
6	B
7	C

MC 37: Emission and Absorption Spectra

Question	Answer
1	B
2	C
3	B
4	E
5	D

MC 38: Lasers and Semiconductors

Question	Answer
1	D
2	E
3	C
4	C
5	E
6	E
7	C

MC 40: Nuclear Changes

Question	Answer
1	C
2	A
3	E
4	B
5	D
6	D
7	E